Exploring

EARTH AND SPACE SCIENCE

9

PRO–STA

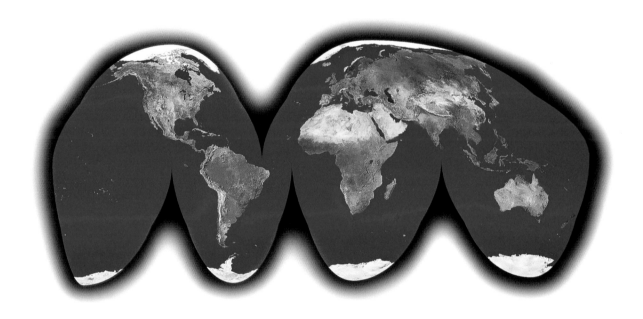

Marshall Cavendish

New York • London • Toronto • Sydney

Marshall Cavendish Corporation
99 White Plains Road
Tarrytown, New York 10591

Website: www.marshallcavendish.com

© 2002 Marshall Cavendish Corporation

Created by **Brown Partworks Limited**

Library of Congress Cataloging-in-Publication Data

Exploring earth and space science.
    p. cm.
    Includes bibliographical references and indexes.
    Contents: 1. Acid and base-Calcium -- 2. Calendar-Continental shelf -- 3. Copper-El
Niño and La Niña -- 4. Energy-Gondwana -- 5. Grassland-Laser -- 6. Light-Meteor -- 7.
Meteorology-Ordovician period -- 8. Ore-Prospecting -- 9. Protein-Star -- 10.
Stratosphere-X ray -- 11. Index.
    ISBN 0-7614-7219-3 (set) -- ISBN 0-7614-7220-7 (v. 1) -- ISBN 0-7614-7221-5 (v. 2)
-- ISBN 0-7614-7222-3 (v. 3) -- ISBN 0-7614-7223-1 (v. 4) -- ISBN 0-7614-7224-X (v.
5) -- ISBN 0-7614-7225-8 (v. 6) -- ISBN 0-7614-7226-6 (v. 7) -- ISBN 0-7614-7227-4
(v. 8) -- ISBN 0-7614-7228-2 (v. 9) -- ISBN 0-7614-7229-0 (v. 10) -- ISBN
0-7614-7230-4 (v. 11)
    1. Earth sciences--Encyclopedias. 2. Space sciences--Encyclopedias. 3.
Astronomy--Encyclopedias

QE5 .E96 2002

550'.3--dc21   00-065801
                                                                                        CIP
                                                                                         AC

ISBN 0-7614-7219-3 (set)

ISBN 0-7614-7228-2 (vol. 9)

Printed in Hong Kong

06 05 04 03 02 01 00   5 4 3 2 1

PHOTOGRAPHIC CREDITS

Corbis: *718*, Jonathan Blair *702*, Doug Wilson *662*, World Panoramas *652–53*
Image Bank: Michael Melford *679*, Colin Molyneux *665*, Thomas Schmitt *678*, Avis Upitis *692*,
Joseph Van Os *672*
NASA: *664* (left), *664* (right), *668–69*, *681*, *682–83*, *683*, *694–95*, *696*, *699*, *712–13*, NSSDC Photo
Gallery *647*, *716–17*
Pictor: *660–61*, *684*
Science Photo Library: *715*, Mike Angliolo *646*, Martin Bond *650*, Dr. Jeremy Burgess *677*, Colin
Cuthbert *714*, Luke Dodd *709*, Richard Folwell *701*, Simon Fraser *693*, Mark Garlick *666*, Pascal
Goetgheluck *690–1*, Eric Grave *700*, Dr. Kenneth Holmes *644–45*, Institute of Oceanographic
Studies *705*, Jean-Loup Charmet *655*, Adams Jones *686*, Maximilian Stock Ltd. *676*, Peter Menzel
708, NASA *711*, Novosti *654*, *674*, *675*, *681*, David Nunuk *658*, David Parker *659*, Alfred Pasieka,
Detlev Van Ravenswaay *698*, Dr. Morely Read *707*, Space Telescope Science *651*, Dr. Robert Spicer
671, Sinclair Stammers *670*, *689*, Sheila Terry *656–57*, Dr. David Wexler *648–49*

Front cover: Dishes of a large radio telescope (Science Photo Library, David Nanuk)

Title page: Projection of Earth's land and oceans (Science Photo Library, Worldsat
            International and J. Knighton)

Back cover: White light being split into a spectrum by a prism (Marshall Cavendish)

Exploring
EARTH AND SPACE SCIENCE

9

PRO–STA

Marshall Cavendish
New York • London • Toronto • Sydney

Protein

Biological polymer that consists of long chains of amino acids

Proteins are large biological molecules called polymers that play essential roles in all living organisms. Like all polymers, proteins are made of many units linked together. There are millions of different types of proteins but only two major groups: structural proteins and biologically active proteins. Structural proteins are used as building blocks for hair, muscle, skin, and many other tissues. Biologically active proteins are essential to nearly every chemical reaction in a living organism. They react with certain chemicals, enabling them to regulate (control) specific chemical reactions or bind to living cells.

Amino acids

The small units that make up proteins are amino acids. There are about 20 different types of amino acids found in proteins, called common or essential amino acids. When proteins are made, the amino acids join together in chains. The order of different amino acids along the chain determines the shape of a protein molecule, which in turn determines the properties of the protein. Short chains of up to 50 amino acids are called polypeptides; longer chains are proteins.

Protein structure

Many protein molecules have enormous, complex, three-dimensional structures. Protein structure is described on four different levels:

primary, secondary, tertiary (TUHR-shee-UH-ree), and quaternary (kwuh-TUHR-nuh-ree).

The primary structure of a protein is the sequence (order) of amino acids along a polypeptide chain. The amino acids are joined by covalent (KOH-VAY-luhnt; shared electron) bonds called peptide bonds, which form when the amino group (NH_2) of one amino acid bonds to the carboxyl group (COOH) of another.

Polypeptide chains fold or curl up to form a protein's secondary structure. This is held together by weak hydrogen bonds, which are easily broken by heat or by certain chemicals. The most common secondary structure is called an alpha helix (HEE-lihks), in which the polypeptide coils up into a springlike shape. The protein in human hair—keratin—contains many of these structures. When human hair is heated, the hydrogen bonds break, allowing the hair to be curled or straightened. When the hair cools, the hydrogen bonds re-form, fixing the style.

The other main type of secondary structure is called a beta-pleated sheet. In this sheet, a long chain of amino acids folds up by hairpin bends. Beta-pleated sheets are strong. They are found in a reptile's scales and a spider's web.

The tertiary structure of a protein is formed by the way beta-pleated sheets and alpha

Computer-generated image showing the makeup of actin, a protein present in muscles. Each colored section represents an amino acid.

helices pack together. Many biologically active proteins are globular (rounded) and contain beta-pleated sheets and alpha helices packed tightly into a ball and held together by a variety of bonds.

Many proteins consist of several polypeptides with their secondary and tertiary shapes entwined. This is the protein's quaternary structure. For example, the protein hemoglobin (HEE-muh-GLOH-buhn; the oxygen-carrying molecule that gives blood its red color) consists of four linked globular chains.

Genes make proteins

The human body contains millions of different proteins. The recipe book for making all these complex molecules is stored in the genes (JEENZ) in the form of deoxyribonucleic acid (DNA). DNA is stored in the cell's nucleus (center).

Just like proteins, DNA molecules are polymers. However, the DNA chain contains only four different types of units, arranged with a particular sequence of three units representing each amino acid.

When a cell needs to make a particular protein, a copy of a gene is made in the nucleus as a molecule called mRNA, which is similar to DNA. The mRNA passes out of the cell's nucleus and is transported to a tiny structure called a ribosome in the cytoplasm (SY-toh-plazm; cell fluid). Here, amino acids are arranged according to the mRNA code. The amino acids are carried by molecules called tRNA. Each tRNA molecule carries one specific amino acid and holds it in the place coded by the mRNA. As the amino acids are positioned, they stick to each other, building up into a new polypeptide chain.

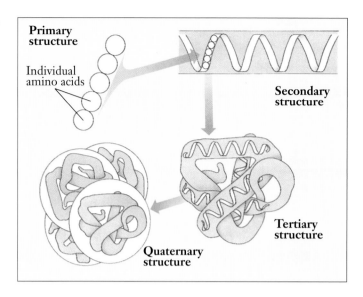

The shape of a protein is determined by the sequence of amino acids along its polypeptide chains.

Protein function

Some proteins are used to build tough body tissues, others are poisons, and still others store substances or carry molecules around the body. Among the most important proteins in the body are hormones, antibodies, and enzymes. Hormones are chemical messengers that trigger changes in the body, such as growth and sexual development. Antibodies are proteins that attack germs, such as bacteria, which cause disease. Enzymes are catalysts (KA-tuh-lists; substances that change the rate of chemical reactions).

Many proteins have been put to use by people. Biological laundry detergents, for example, contain enzymes that help digest stains. During plastic surgery, collagen (KAH-luh-juhn; the protein that gives shape to the ears and nose) is injected into parts of the body such as the lips to change their size. Both silk and wool are made of proteins, and numerous drugs are polypeptides.

The way a protein acts depends on its shape. If this shape is denatured (changed) by heat, for example, the protein changes. Some proteins change irreversibly when they are denatured. For example, albumen (AL-byoo-muhn), in egg white, becomes opaque (oh-PAYK; cloudy) when denatured—so eggs change color when cooked.

CHECK THESE OUT!
✔CATALYST ✔ORGANIC CHEMISTRY ✔POLYMER

Proton

All matter is made of atoms, and atoms consist of three types of particles: protons, neutrons, and electrons. Protons are tiny particles found in the nuclei (NOO-klee-eye; centers) of atoms, along with neutrons. Electrons orbit (move around) the nuclei, and so make up the outer part of atoms.

Protons and electrons have equal but opposite charges: protons are positive and electrons are negative. Neutrons have no charge. The electrons in an atom are attracted to its protons because opposite charges attract each other. This attraction helps to hold the atom together. The neutrons in the nucleus also help to hold the atom together. If a nucleus was made up of only protons, it would burst apart because the positive charges would repel (push away) each other. However, neutrons and protons attract each other with a force called the strong nuclear force. This keeps the nucleus stable (together).

An atom in its normal state has the same number of protons and electrons. The charges balance each other and the atom is neutral. If an atom loses electrons, the atom takes on a positive charge because there are more protons than electrons. Such charged atoms are called cations (KAT-EYE-uhnz; positive ions). Similarly, atoms can take on extra electrons to become anions (AN-EYE-uhnz; negative ions).

Chemists define an element by the number of protons its atoms contain. This is called the atomic number. Hydrogen has an atomic number of 1 because its atom has a single proton

This picture shows the nucleus of an atom as a cluster of protons and neutrons. Electrons orbit the nucleus.

with one electron orbiting it. At the other extreme, uranium has an atomic number of 92 (92 protons and 92 electrons). The periodic table lists elements in order of their atomic number.

Discovering protons

The first person to find evidence that protons are distinct particles was German physicist Wilhelm Wien (1864–1928). He carried out an experiment in which hydrogen atoms were stripped of their electrons by an electrical field, leaving naked protons. Wien was able to fire these protons at a fluorescent (floo-REH-suhnt; glowing) screen, which lit up when the protons hit it. By measuring how much magnetism or electricity was needed to deflect the beam, he worked out the mass of the protons. He found it was nearly 2,000 times greater than the mass of electrons. It is now known that nearly all the mass of atoms is contained in their protons and neutrons.

CHECK THESE OUT!
✔ATOM ✔ELECTRON ✔ELEMENT ✔ION ✔MASS
✔NEUTRON ✔PARTICLE PHYSICS ✔PERIODIC TABLE

Pulsar

A rapidly rotating neutron star that emits beams of radiation

Rapidly spinning stars that send out pulses of intense radiation are called pulsars. These pulses create a "cosmic lighthouse"—a star that appears to blink rapidly on and off.

Pulsars were first detected in 1967 by English radio astronomers Antony Hewish (born 1924) and Jocelyn Bell Burnell (born 1943). They picked up a precisely timed radio signal from space, with pulses so regular that some astronomers thought it was artificial. The first pulsar was codenamed LGM 1 (Little Green Man 1) because scientists thought it might be a deliberate signal from an alien civilization. However, in 1968, Thomas Gold of Cornell University suggested pulsars might be neutron stars, the collapsed cores of giant stars that have destroyed themselves in huge explosions.

Supernovas

When a giant star, many times more massive than the Sun, reaches the end of its life, it throws off most of its material in a huge supernova explosion. The star leaves behind a core that no longer generates energy and so cannot hold itself up against its own gravity. This core collapses rapidly, and the pressure that builds up is so great that atoms are split apart and subatomic particles combine until the star is made almost entirely of small uncharged particles called neutrons. A neutron star is the densest object in the Universe. It has the mass of a star such as the Sun crammed into a sphere just a few miles across.

As the star collapses, its rate of rotation speeds up—just as a spinning ice skater speeds up as she pulls in her arms and concentrates her mass in one place. Neutron stars can have incredible rotation rates, up to a thousand revolutions each second. At the same time, the star's collapse concentrates and intensifies its magnetic field. Electrically charged particles get ripped from the surface of the star, and the magnetic north and south poles form two intense beams repelling this matter away from the star. If the magnetic field is tilted at an angle to the star's axis of rotation, these beams sweep around with every rotation, creating the "lighthouse" effect of a pulsar.

Pulsar rates

The youngest-known pulsar lies at the heart of the Crab Nebula, the remains of a supernova explosion observed by Chinese astronomers in 1054. The Crab Pulsar is a neutron star 6 miles (10 km) across, spinning 30 times per second. It gives off radio waves, visible light, X rays, and high-energy gamma rays. Although an individual pulsar's behavior is very predictable, and it gradually slows down over millions of years, slow-spinning pulsars are not necessarily the oldest, because the pulsar's initial rate of spin depends on the size of the original star.

CHECK THESE OUT!
✔ASTRONOMY ✔CONSTELLATION ✔GALAXY ✔HUBBLE SPACE TELESCOPE ✔QUASAR ✔STAR

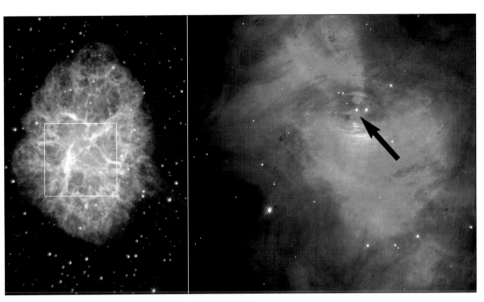

At the center of the Crab Nebula (near left) lies the Crab Pulsar (arrowed). This star is only six miles wide.

Quantum Theory

The fundamental theory of physics that describes matter and radiation

Objects in everyday life tend to behave according to a set of rules that were first outlined in the 17th century. Classical physics, as these rules are called, was unchallenged until the early 20th century. Although classical physics still applies in most situations, it cannot explain many things that happen in the miniature world of atoms and subatomic particles (the particles that make up atoms). Just as the theory of relativity was needed to explain the behavior of matter at high speeds and in intense gravitational fields, so a new theory was required to explain the atomic world—quantum theory.

Packets of energy

One of the most important ideas in quantum theory is that matter can absorb or emit electromagnetic energy only in packets called quanta (each one is called a quantum). Dealing in quanta is a bit like buying cookies—a person cannot buy a few cookies out of a packet, only whole packets. In the same way, atoms can take in or give out energy only in whole quanta.

Quantum theory also assumes that particles of matter can exhibit wavelike behavior under some conditions. An electron, for example, might behave like a particle in collision with another electron, but behaves more like a wave when it is orbiting the nucleus. Whether wave or particle behavior is observed depends on the experiment being done. This is called wave-particle duality.

The quantum world

Classical physics is confirmed by almost everything that happens in everyday life,

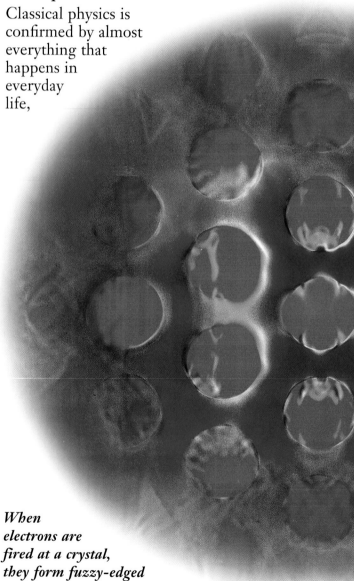

When electrons are fired at a crystal, they form fuzzy-edged patterns similar to the blurred edges of shadows formed by light waves. This shows that matter can behave as waves, which is an important part of quantum theory.

HIGHLIGHTS

◆ Quantum theory has replaced classical physics as an explanation of matter and radiation, especially the world of atoms and even smaller particles.

◆ An important idea in quantum theory is that matter can absorb or emit electromagnetic energy only in small packets called quanta.

◆ Quantum theory explains how light and matter behave as both waves and particles.

from the workings of a jet engine to an acrobat's movement. The world of subatomic particles is not so easy to observe.

Despite this difficulty, physicists have found important evidence for quantum theory. When hot objects absorb or give out heat radiation, they deal in the fixed packets of energy that quantum theory predicts. Another piece of evidence comes from the photoelectric effect. This involves the ejection of electrons from certain materials when light shines on them, and it can be explained by quantum theory.

The quantum theory is also supported by an important experiment called the Compton effect. When light passes through certain materials, it comes out with less energy than it had to begin with. Some energy is lost because photons (FOH-tahnz; packets of light) collide with electrons in the atoms of the material. The amount of energy that is lost is the amount expected if the quantum theory is applied.

A final piece of evidence comes from spectroscopy, which is a way of identifying atoms and molecules using the light they give off. When a substance is heated, its atoms or molecules give off light (or other electromagnetic radiation) of certain colors. (Color is determined by wavelength – the distance between one wave crest and the next.) This is because an atom or molecule can take in or give out only fixed quanta of energy. Quanta of different sizes are seen as light of different colors. Quanta with

LOOK CLOSER

Uncertainty Principle

The uncertainty principle was proposed in 1927 by German physicist Werner Karl Heisenberg (1901–1976). He said that it is impossible to work out the position and speed of a small particle. To do this, someone would need to look at the particle in light. However, when a photon of light hits the particle, it changes the particle's speed and position, making a precise measurement impossible. Heisenberg showed that the quantum world is unpredictable, unlike the world of classical physics.

more energy produce radiation with shorter wavelengths. This radiation can be observed very accurately using a spectroscope.

Quantum scientists

The quantum theory was the result of the efforts of many different people. In 1900, German physicist Max Planck (1858–1947) laid the foundations when he published a paper explaining how objects take in or give out only fixed amounts of energy. That idea was expanded by German-born U.S. physicist Albert Einstein (1879–1955). Einstein showed how light could be thought of as a particle of energy called a photon, not just as a wave as people thought.

In 1913, Danish physicist Niels Bohr (1885–1962) suggested the modern view of an atom with electrons in fixed energy levels around a central nucleus containing protons and neutrons. However, Bohr himself did not come to believe in quantum theory until much later.

French physicist Louis-Victor-Pierre-Raymond de Broglie (1892–1987) explained in detail how matter can act both as a particle and a wave. Austrian physicist Erwin Schrödinger (1887–1961) worked out a complex equation showing how a particle can behave as a wave.

CHECK THESE OUT!

✔ELECTRON ✔LIGHT ✔MATTER ✔NEWTONIAN PHYSICS ✔PARTICLE PHYSICS ✔PHOTOELECTRIC EFFECT ✔RELATIVITY ✔SPECTROSCOPY

Quartz

A hard mineral made of silicon and oxygen

Quartz makes up about 12 percent of Earth's crust, and it is common in a great variety of rocks. The word *quartz* is a shortened version of *Querklufterz*—the name that German miners gave to white veins of quartz running through the rocks. This common mineral is a type of silica (silicon dioxide, SiO_2).

Physical properties

Quartz is hard enough to blunt a knife. The mineral's crystals are often perfect six-sided (hexagonal) prisms. These may break to give an uneven surface or one that is curved like broken glass. Usually quartz is milky white or it can be colorless and transparent (named rock crystal). However, impurities such as manganese or iron can color the mineral. Amethyst (A-muh-thist) is purple quartz, cairngorm (KAIRN-gawrm) is dark brown, and rose quartz is pink. These varieties are used as semiprecious gemstones in jewelry and other ornaments.

Formation of quartz

Crystals of quartz form when hot fluids deep in Earth's crust rise into cracks and faults. Crystals grow from the fluids as they cool. When lava or magma (liquid rock) cool, quartz crystals form and help to make igneous rocks.

Quartz in rocks

Quartz is found in many igneous rocks, especially those such as granite that have much silica in them. Granite contains 30 percent quartz, seen as small, gray grains. As the quartz forms directly from magma, it is not colored by impurities.

When quartz grains are broken from rocks such as granite, they build up in rivers and the sea as layers of sand. Eventually, after perhaps millions of years, these layers become cemented together to make sandstone. Sandstone is an example of a sedimentary rock. Other sedimentary rocks such as shale and clay may also contain some quartz.

Quartz is also found in metamorphic rocks. These rocks are made from other rocks when heat and pressure change them deep underground. Because quartz is a very stable mineral, it remains unchanged through the process of metamorphism. Therefore, metamorphic rocks such as gneiss (NYS) and slate contain much quartz.

Uses of quartz

Quartz crystals are known to vibrate at very regular intervals when electric charges are sent through them. This property makes them ideal for use in microelectronics. Quartz watches contain very small quartz crystals that vibrate at a definite frequency and so help the watch to keep accurate time. Quartz is also the main part of sand used in the building industry. Another very important use for quartz is in glassmaking.

CHECK THESE OUT!
✔CRYSTAL ✔IGNEOUS ROCK ✔METAMORPHIC ROCK ✔MINERALOGY ✔ROCK ✔SAND ✔SEDIMENTARY ROCK

Pure quartz is colorless, but impurities can color the crystals white, pink, yellow, blue, green, and smoky brown.

Quasar

A brilliant object in space that looks like a star but is billions of light-years away

Quasars (KWAY-ZAHRZ) are some of the most mysterious objects in the Universe. They are starlike points of light that are billions of light-years away—tiny, and yet incredibly bright.

In 1960, astronomers discovered this new type of astronomical object when, using radio telescopes, they found a starlike object called 3C 48 that was emitting radio waves. Some astronomers thought they had discovered a strange new type of star, while others thought that the "quasi-stellar" object (shortened to *quasar*) was actually a huge distant galaxy. This idea was soon dismissed because the energy produced by the quasar changed rapidly from day to day. Energy changes could not possibly spread through an area larger than a few billion miles across in the observed time. The quasar's power source, therefore, must be relatively tiny.

Quasar mystery

As astronomers began to search for other quasars, the mystery deepened. They found quasars emitting X rays and visible light as well as radio waves, and some that did not produce radio waves at all. Stars shine mostly in visible light and, although some kind of radio star might be possible, no star could possibly be hot enough to shine purely in X rays.

When Dutch astronomer Maarten Schmidt (born 1929) split the light from quasars into a rainbow-like spectrum, he found that it was very highly redshifted (appeared redder than expected). This meant that quasars were moving rapidly

The bright center of this spiral galaxy is a quasar named PG 0052+251. It is 1.4 billion light-years away from Earth.

away from Earth—at speeds of 80 percent the speed of light. According to astronomical theory, the faster an object is receding (moving away), the farther away it is, so quasars are the most distant objects in the Universe. Their light takes billions of years to reach Earth. Therefore, quasars existed in the early days of the Universe and must be incredibly hot radiation sources. Since these first discoveries, astronomers have found even older quasars with higher redshifts.

What are quasars?

Most astronomers agree that a quasar is a young and violent galaxy. Most galaxies, including the Milky Way, are thought to form with huge black holes at their centers. The intense gravity of these black holes pulls in any material that gets too close and can rip stars apart. By the time a galaxy has settled down, the central black hole has swept an empty space around it, keeping stars at a distance. Astronomers think quasars are young galaxies in which the black hole is still swallowing nearby stars. As material spirals down into the black hole, its molecules and atoms are ripped apart, heating up to incredible temperatures so they emit X rays and the other types of radiation that can be seen from Earth.

Some astronomers disagree with this theory. They think that quasars could be fast-moving objects much closer to Earth. They point to quasars apparently linked to nearby objects with much lower redshifts as evidence for this theory.

CHECK THESE OUT!
✔ASTRONOMY ✔BLACK HOLE ✔DOPPLER EFFECT ✔GALAXY ✔LIGHT ✔MILKY WAY ✔RADIO WAVE ✔STAR ✔UNIVERSE ✔X RAY

Quaternary Period

The most recent period of geological time

The Quaternary period, part of the Cenozoic era, contains two epochs (E-puhks), the Pleistocene and Holocene (sometimes called Recent). So far, the Quaternary has lasted for 1.6 million years. During this time, ice sheets and glaciers frequently covered much of the Northern Hemisphere, including Europe and North America. Importantly, the human species, *Homo sapiens*, also evolved and spread over Earth.

Quaternary ice age

The ice age of the Quaternary has occurred in cycles of cold glacial episodes and warmer interglacial periods, which were sometimes warmer than today's climate. Around 120,000 years ago, animals such as hippopotamuses and lions lived in northern Europe. Then there was a very cold phase when ice sheets and glaciers spread into Europe, Asia, Canada, New England, and the midwestern part of the United States.

Animals that could withstand the cold, such as woolly mammoths, bears, wolves, bisons, and arctic foxes, flourished just to the south of the ice sheets. The Bering Strait in northwestern North America was dry land at this time, and animals could migrate from Asia to North America. About 20 cycles of cold and warm climates took place during the Pleistocene epoch, the first part of the Quaternary period, which started as the climate began to get colder.

Global warming and sea levels

The warmer, stable climate of the Holocene epoch that exists now may be only a short interglacial period, and the ice sheets may return in another 20,000 years or so. People are causing weather changes as human activity produces global warming.

When the ice sheets were at their biggest, more of Earth's water was locked away as ice. Therefore, the sea levels were lower around the world. In some areas, the great weight of ice on the land pushed down large areas toward sea level. As the ice melted, these landmasses rose up again. In many coastal areas, there are ancient raised beaches showing how the land has risen out of the sea. Today's sea levels are rising in many places as ice sheets melt and add water to the oceans. With an increase in global warming, this rise is set to continue.

Ice sheets

The Quaternary ice sheets spread as far south as Kansas in North America. There were four major glaciations (ice advances) separated by warm interglacial periods. Recent research has found evidence of

Ice age glaciers carved deep, wide valleys. This flooded glacial valley is called a fjord.

HIGHLIGHTS

◆ The Quaternary is the most recent geological period. It contains the divisions of geologic time called the Pleistocene and Holocene epochs.

◆ The Quaternary period began about 1.6 million years ago.

◆ Humans developed during the Quaternary.

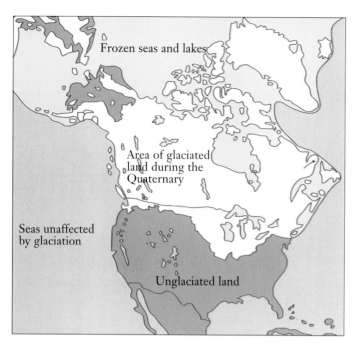

The advance of ice sheets (white areas) in North America and Greenland during the Quaternary.

many more less severe ice advances. However, geologists are finding it difficult to work out the history of the glaciations because the deposits of one ice advance are removed by the next.

Ice advances have a massive effect on the landscape. They leave behind huge masses of sediment, which is eroded as the glaciers move and deposited when they melt. This sediment forms hills and often causes rivers to change their course. The Great Lakes in North America were formed when glacial deposits dammed river systems. At its height, the ice sheet covered all the Great Lakes area and left moraine (muh-RAYN; glacial deposit) when it melted.

In Europe, the sea level was low enough to allow migration of animals across the English Channel. High mountain ranges, as in Scotland, were heavily eroded (worn away) to produce sharp pyramidlike peaks with deep, U-shaped valleys between them. Moraines left across the valley acted as dams, allowing mountain lakes to form when

the ice melted. Coastlines that were covered with glaciers, such as northern Canada, Scandinavia, or Siberia, are very jagged because valleys formed by glaciers have been flooded by the sea, creating sea lochs, fjords (fee-AWRDS), and inlets.

Living with ice

The ice ages caused many extinctions of certain species (types) of living organisms, allowing other species to develop and evolve. For example, during the Pleistocene, the very large plant-eating land mammals that had flourished during the earlier part of the Quaternary became extinct. Possibly the climatic changes led to food plants dying out. However, the genus Homo flourished during the Quaternary. The oldest creatures that can be called human are the Neanderthals, a subspecies of humans called *Homo sapiens neanderthalensis*. These humans probably lived at the same time as *Homo erectus*, a humanlike animal. Apart from their heavier skull and craggy eyebrows, Neanderthals were very like modern humans. They lived in central and Mediterranean Europe around 40,000 years ago. Why they disappeared is a bit of a puzzle. About 90,000 years ago, modern humans (another subspecies called *Homo sapiens sapiens*) moved into areas where the Neanderthals lived and appeared to wipe them out.

CHECK THESE OUT!
✔CENOZOIC ERA ✔GEOLOGIC TIMESCALE
✔GLACIER ✔GLOBAL WARMING ✔ICE AGE

Radioactivity

The release of small particles and energy by unstable atoms

People often think of radioactivity (the release of radiation by disintegrating atoms) as unnatural. Atomic bombs and nuclear accidents, such as the one in Chernobyl (chuhr-NOH-buhl), Ukraine, in 1986, introduce into the environment radioactivity that would not otherwise have been there. However, radioactivity is also released by natural processes. Many natural substances are constantly changing into other substances by a process called radioactive decay, which releases radioactivity. Radioactivity can be dangerous, but its discovery has brought many benefits to humans, including nuclear energy and a type of cancer treatment called radiation therapy.

What causes radioactivity?

The nucleus (center) of an atom is made up of protons, which have a positive electric charge, and neutrons, which have no charge. The atoms of most chemical elements exist in several different forms called isotopes. All isotopes of one element have the same number of protons but different numbers of neutrons. Some isotopes are more stable than others. The less stable ones break up into more stable atoms and give off radiation. For example, carbon 14 (an isotope of carbon containing six protons and eight neutrons) behaves in this way. Carbon 14 is radioactive. It emits beta particles to become nitrogen 14, which is stable.

Alpha, beta, and gamma radioactivity

There are three different types of radioactivity: alpha, beta, and gamma. An alpha particle is exactly the same as the nucleus of a helium atom and is made up of two protons and two neutrons. Alpha particles are relatively massive and

The remains of the Chernobyl nuclear reactor that exploded in 1986, spreading radioactivity.

HIGHLIGHTS

◆ There are three common types of radioactivity—alpha, beta, and gamma radiation.

◆ An alpha particle is a helium nucleus, a beta particle is an electron, and a gamma ray is a type of high-energy electromagnetic radiation.

◆ Radioactivity was discovered by Antoine-Henri Becquerel in 1896 and investigated thoroughly by Marie and Pierre Curie.

DISCOVERERS

Marie Curie

By the 1920s, Marie Curie had become the first world-famous female scientist. Born Marie Sklowdowska in Poland in 1867, she studied physics and chemistry at the Sorbonne in Paris. In 1895, Marie married chemist Pierre Curie. Their most important joint achievement was the thorough investigation of radioactivity (named by Marie).

The Curies went on to discover the radioactive elements radium and polonium (named for Marie's homeland). When Pierre was killed in a road accident in 1906, Marie continued alone and achieved the isolation of small amounts of pure radium.

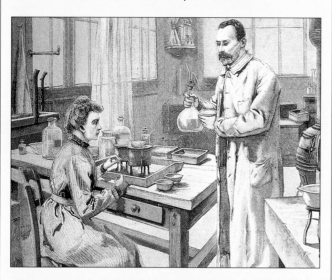

Marie and Pierre Curie. Years of exposure to radium led to Marie's death from blood cancer.

potentially damaging to living cells. Fortunately, they quickly pick up electrons from any matter they encounter to become relatively harmless helium gas. They can be brought to a halt by something as flimsy as a sheet of paper. The two protons in an alpha particle are positively charged, and so the path of alpha particles can be bent using electric or magnetic fields. All the isotopes of uranium (U) emit alpha particles.

Beta particles are exactly the same as electrons. Because they are smaller, they are less likely to be neutralized immediately than alpha particles, but they can be stopped by thin metal foil. Although beta particles are usually negatively charged (like electrons), positively charged beta particles also exist. These are called positrons. Cobalt 60, used to treat cancer, emits beta particles. The artificial isotope carbon 11 emits positrons.

Gamma radiation is the third type of radioactivity. Unlike alpha and beta radiation, gamma rays are not particles. They are a type of electromagnetic radiation such as light, X rays, and microwaves. Therefore, they travel at the speed of light. Because they have very high energies (even higher than X rays), gamma rays travel considerable distances through space. Some types of gamma radiation can be stopped by a thin sheet of metal, whereas more energetic gamma rays may be able to penetrate a thick piece of lead. Almost every isotope that emits alpha or beta particles also emits gamma rays.

The discovery of radioactivity

Radioactivity was discovered by accident in 1896 by French physicist Antoine-Henri Becquerel (1852–1908), who was trying to find out whether uranium would give off X rays. He placed a sample of uranium on top of a covered photographic plate (like a film) and later found a pattern of shadows on the plate. He could explain this only if some sort of radiation were being given off by the uranium.

The most famous investigator of radioactivity was Polish-born French physicist Marie Curie (1867–1934), who, with husband Pierre Curie (1859–1906), discovered radioactive elements. Their work involved separating tiny samples of radioactive substances from huge amounts of ore. In four years, they extracted a few hundredths of an ounce of a radioactive substance called radium chloride from 9 tons (8.8 tonnes) of uranium ore.

Radiation was better understood after English physicist Ernest Rutherford (1871–1937) "split the atom," showing that atoms were made up of protons and neutrons. His experiments also confirmed that alpha particles were really helium nuclei and that beta particles were electrons.

CHECK THESE OUT!
✔ATOM ✔FISSION ✔FUSION ✔ISOTOPE ✔NUCLEAR PHYSICS ✔PLUTONIUM ✔RADIOCARBON DATING

Radiocarbon Dating

Using radioactive carbon to work out the age of the remains of living organisms

By studying radioactivity in rocks and other material, it is possible to find out how old they are and when certain events happened. Once-living matter can be dated using a process of this type, called radiocarbon dating.

What is radioactivity?

Many elements decay (break down) with time into different elements. As this happens, radiation is given off as alpha or beta particles and gamma rays. Different radioactive elements make different amounts of radiation. Some decay faster than others. The rate of decay is described as the half-life. A half-life period is the time taken for half of the atoms in a radioactive element to decay and is always the same, no matter how many radioactive atoms are present.

Checking dates

Half-life periods vary. Uranium 238 (an isotope of uranium) has a half-life of 4.5 billion years, and carbon 14 (an isotope of carbon) has a half-life period of 5,730 years. Geologists use the radioactivity of these elements locked away in rock minerals to date rocks. A geologic timescale has been established, based on this work.

Some of the methods used can date rocks hundreds of millions of years old. Radiocarbon dating, because of carbon 14's relatively short

Each tree ring contains a record of how much carbon 14 was around in that year of the tree's life.

half-life, can only be used with accuracy back into the last ice age, up to about 60,000 years ago. It is very useful in dating material such as wood and remains from other living organisms.

Carbon isotopes

Carbon 14 is called a cosmogenic (KAHZ-muh-JEH-nik) isotope. Cosmogenic isotopes are those that are always being made as cosmic rays from

HIGHLIGHTS

◆ Radioactivity is the natural breakdown of certain elements into other elements.

◆ Carbon 14 is a radioactive element often used to date objects that were once alive.

◆ Dating an object using the known rate of decay of carbon 14 is called radiocarbon dating.

outer space hit Earth. Therefore, there will always be a certain amount of carbon 14 on Earth and this amount is not continuously decreasing, as is the case for uranium (U).

Carbon is used in all living bodies because it can build the very large molecules that make up plant and animal tissues. Most of this carbon is carbon 12, but about one atom in a trillion is carbon 14. Plants and animals absorb this carbon 14 from the atmosphere or seawater. When an organism dies, it no longer takes in carbon 14 and so the amount of carbon 14 compared to carbon 12 goes down as the carbon 14 breaks down. The U.S. chemist Willard Libby (1908–1980) was the first scientist to realize that this process could be used to date items of biological material from long ago.

First attempts
Libby tested his theory in 1947 by using samples whose age was already known by archaeologists (AHR-kee-AH-luh-jists; scientists who study the remains of past human life). His samples were large, and he broke them down to leave only the carbon residue. He measured the radioactivity of his samples and calculated their age taking natural, background radiation into account. His earliest work came close to the expected ages.

However, when carbon 14 dating was attempted on Egyptian material dating from about 2500 B.C.E., there was a difference between the carbon 14 dates and those calculated from historical study. Scientists discovered that there was a change in the amount of carbon 14 in the atmosphere. This is linked to variations in

Earth's magnetic field. Between 4,000 and 5,000 years ago, a change in the magnetic field affected the rate at which cosmic rays reach the atmosphere and create carbon 14. To use radiocarbon dating accurately, scientists need to know how much carbon 14 is in the atmosphere.

Tree rings
Each year, many trees make a new growth ring around their stems as they grow. A trunk cross-section shows these rings as concentric (having the same center) circles in the wood. Each year's growth absorbs the carbon 14 for that year, and the older rings contain a record of how much carbon 14 was around in previous years. By counting back from the most recent ring, scientists get an accurate date of each ring, and each year's carbon 14 amount.

In California, bristlecone pine trees live for more than 4,000 years and remain standing long after they die. By using trees such as this, scientists have been able to count back each year for up to 8,000 years. This science is called dendrochronology (DEN-DROH-kruh-NAH-luh-jee) and has helped to make radiocarbon dating much more accurate.

New developments
Radiocarbon dating originally required a large sample of material that contained enough carbon for a Geiger counter (a machine that measures radiation) to measure radioactivity for a few days. It has been found that by using a mass spectrometer (a machine that can detect the isotopes in a substance), a smaller sample can be used for a shorter time.

Radiocarbon dating can only be used for material that was once alive. Some material gives better results than others. Bones may give poor results because they deteriorate in hot, dry climates. Wood in the center of a tree may cease to absorb carbon 14 for many years before it is cut down. Nevertheless, carbon 14 age dating has been used with great success for dating items well into the last ice age.

CHECK THESE OUT!
✔COSMIC RAY ✔GEOLOGIC TIMESCALE ✔ISOTOPE ✔ORGANIC CHEMISTRY ✔RADIOACTIVITY

Radio Wave

Electromagnetic wave used to send information at the speed of light

Radio is one of the most important methods of transmitting information from place to place. It provides thousands of radio broadcasts, television transmissions, and long-distance telephone conversations. Radio is at the heart of the cellular telephone system and two-way radio. It also offers a way of "seeing" objects that would otherwise be invisible: a system called radar helps airplanes and ships to navigate (find their way) without colliding with other sea and air traffic, and radio telescopes enable astronomers to see deep into space. All of these things are made possible by radio waves.

What are radio waves?

Just like light, infrared radiation, and microwaves, radio waves are a type of electromagnetic radiation and so travel through space at the speed of light (186,282 miles per second, or 299,792 km/s). However, radio waves have a much longer wavelength (the distance from one wave peak to the next) than light waves. Typical radio waves have a wavelength ranging from 62 miles (100 km) to less than ½ inch (1 cm). The frequency of radio waves (the number of waves passing a certain point in a second) varies from a few thousand to several billion waves per second.

Radio waves are useful for transmitting information because their long wavelength enables them to travel around obstacles in a way that light waves cannot. Radio waves are reflected by a part of Earth's atmosphere called the ionosphere, allowing the waves to be transmitted across thousands of miles. The ionosphere acts like a gigantic spherical mirror surrounding Earth that bounces radio waves from one place to another across the surface of the planet.

AM and FM

Transmitting information with waves is similar to the way light is used to give different types of information. Changing the color of light (changing its frequency) is one

Dish-shaped antennas used as a giant radio telescope at Owens Valley, California.

way to send information. Traffic signals, for example, use red light for "stop" and green for "go." Information can also be contained in the strength of light (amplitude). For example, the house lights are dimmed in a theater to show that the play is about to begin, while the intense beam of a lighthouse warns sailors not to stray too close to the coast.

Radio waves also send information using changes in frequency and amplitude. A basic wave, called a carrier, is sent from the transmitter (perhaps using a large broadcasting antenna) to the receiver (a transistor radio in a car, for example). Information is coded into this wave in one of two ways. The signal information might be added by constantly changing the strength of the carrier wave. This is called amplitude modulation (AM). Alternatively, the signal can be transmitted by constantly changing the frequency of the carrier wave, called frequency modulation (FM). AM and FM radio stations transmit sound using one of these two methods. Atmospheric interference caused by weather is also picked up by AM receivers but has little effect on FM receivers. This explains why FM radio broadcasts sound clearer and crisper than AM broadcasts.

History of radio

Radio waves were discovered by German physicist Heinrich Hertz (1857–1894) toward the end of the 19th century while he was experimenting with electromagnetism. Hertz found that if he made a large spark between a pair of metal rods on one side of his laboratory, a much smaller spark appeared between a similar pair of rods on the other side of the room. He realized that radio waves traveled from the first set of rods (the transmitter) to the second set of rods (the receiver) through empty space.

The work of Irish-Italian physicist Guglielmo Marconi (1874–1937) transformed radio from a laboratory curiosity into an essential technology. After carrying out experiments in Italy, Marconi moved to England and soon found ways of sending radio signals over longer and longer distances. One of his important discoveries was that a long wire sends signals farther than a short wire. This led to the development of radio antennas (aerials). In 1898, he transmitted radio

LOOK CLOSER — Using Radar

If a man stands some distance from a wall and claps his hands, he hears an echo of the sound some time later. If he knows the speed of sound and how long it takes for the echo to return, he can work out his distance from the wall. Radar (short for *ra*dio *d*etection *an*d *r*anging) is a method of locating objects and obstacles that works in exactly the same way, only using radio waves instead of sound waves. The radar equipment used by ships and airplanes sends out pulses of radio waves from a transmitter and measures the time it takes for the echoes to return. A similar idea is used in a piece of equipment called a Doppler radar, which is used by weather-forecasters to measure where rainstorms are and how quickly they are moving. Archeologists (scientists who study the remains of human life) use radar to locate objects buried beneath the ground.

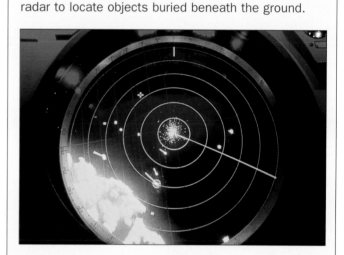

A radar screen on board a tanker shows nearby ships and the coast (yellow area). The tanker's position is the center of the screen.

signals 16 miles (24 km) across the south coast of England and also used antennas hanging from kites to send messages from Cornwall in England to St. John's in Newfoundland, Canada, 2,200 miles (3,500 km) away.

CHECK THESE OUT!
✔DOPPLER EFFECT ✔ELECTROMAGNETIC SPECTRUM
✔IONOSPHERE ✔LIGHT ✔METEOROLOGY
✔MICROWAVE ✔SEMICONDUCTOR

Rainbow

Arch of colors seen in the sky when sunlight falls on a shower of raindrops

Rainbows are caused when light from the Sun passes through a collection of water droplets, for example, rain, spray, fog, or even ice. Although they can be explained quite simply and scientifically, stories are often told about the formation of rainbows. Perhaps because a rainbow appears when the Sun shines through after a shower of rain, it is seen as a symbol of hope in many cultures. The Bible's Old Testament tells how God set a rainbow in the sky after the Great Flood as a promise never to send another flood. There is also a popular story that a pot of gold lies at the foot of every rainbow. However, no one can reach the end of a rainbow, as the effect can be seen only at a distance.

Rainbows only appear in certain conditions. The Sun must break through the clouds after rain, but not be too high in the sky. That is why rainbows are usually seen in the morning or in late afternoon or evening, but rarely at noon. To see a rainbow, a person must stand with his or her back to the Sun, and with steady rain still falling some distance in front. Rainbows also form over waterfalls, where the air is filled with water droplets.

Reflecting and refracting light

A rainbow appears when the Sun's rays shine into individual raindrops, which reflect and refract (bend) the light. Refraction happens when

Sir Isaac Newton divided the fuzzy, colorful band of a rainbow into seven distinct colors. He chose to name them red, orange, yellow, green, blue, indigo, and violet.

HIGHLIGHTS

◆ A rainbow is formed when the Sun's rays are reflected and refracted by a shower of raindrops.

◆ The refraction occurs when light slows down as it passes from air through to water.

◆ White light is made up of a spectrum of colors. The colors split up and become individually visible as light passes through a raindrop.

◆ Some of the colored rays then reflect back off the far side of the raindrop, and are further refracted as they emerge from the near side of the drop.

light passes from air to water, because air and water have different densities. Light rays pass more slowly through water than air, so the rays bend as they enter water. This effect can be seen if you look down at somebody swimming underwater. They appear to have a wobbly outline.

White light from the Sun is made up of a range of colors, including red, orange, yellow, green, blue, indigo, and violet. These colors make up the spectrum. They are seen in a rainbow, and also when light passes through a prism (PRIH-zuhm; a transparent object that separates the different colors in light).

Each color in the spectrum has a different wavelength and so passes through water at a different speed. Blue light passes through more slowly than green, and green more slowly than red. White light splits into this spectrum of colors inside a raindrop because the colored rays bend by different amounts. Red is refracted at an angle of 42 degrees and each following color in the spectrum is bent by a slightly smaller angle. Violet is bent by the smallest angle—about 40 degrees. This means a rainbow is red on the outer edge and violet on the inside edge. Some of the colored rays are then reflected back by the far side of the raindrop. They pass through the raindrop again and emerge from the side nearest the onlooker, who then sees a rainbow.

If the Sun is particularly bright and the distant raindrops are small, a second, fainter rainbow (called the secondary bow) may appear outside the first arch (primary bow). This effect occurs when light rays are reflected twice inside the raindrops. The colors in the second bow appear in reverse order to those in the brightest arch.

Each viewer sees a rainbow from a slightly different position and a different set of rays reach each viewer's eyes. Rainbows have a curved shape because each viewer only sees rays coming from raindrops a certain distance away. If someone tries to approach a rainbow, it seems to move away, because the colors come from a new set of drops. No one can ever reach a rainbow, no matter how fast she or he runs.

Studying rainbows

The colors of the rainbow were named by English scientist, Sir Isaac Newton (1642–1727). Newton was the first to obtain a colored spectrum by shining light through a glass prism. While prisms refract and split white light into the colors of the spectrum in the same way that a raindrop first divides them, the rays do not bounce back to be refracted still more, as happens inside a raindrop. Newton was first and foremost a scientist, but he was also interested in magic. Seven was considered to be a magical number, so Newton identified seven distinct colors in the rainbow.

Rainbows can sometimes be seen in the spray from ornamental fountains. When this happens, the Sun is shining through the spray toward the viewer, generally from high in the sky. The onlooker sees only the first refraction. Circular rainbows are occasionally seen around the Sun or the Moon. These colored circles appear when light passes through tiny ice crystals high in the atmosphere.

CHECK THESE OUT!
✔COLOR ✔DENSITY ✔LIGHT
✔NEWTONIAN PHYSICS
✔SUN ✔WEATHER

Rain, Sleet, and Snow

Types of precipitation that form in clouds and later fall to the ground

Earth's weather is unlike that of any other planet in the Solar System. This is mainly because Earth's atmosphere contains water. Rain, drizzle, snow, sleet, and hail are all different types of precipitation (prih-SIH-puh-TAY-shuhn; water deposited on Earth). They form in clouds and eventually fall to the ground. Rain and drizzle are liquid precipitation. Solid forms of precipitation include snow, sleet, and hail.

The water cycle

Precipitation is part of Earth's water cycle. Water enters the atmosphere from oceans, rivers, lakes, puddles, moist soil, and plants by evaporation. This raises the humidity (moisture content) of the air. Humidity in turn produces clouds, which eventually precipitate. This feeds the lakes, rivers, oceans, and ice fields once more, forming a continuous, cyclical process.

Thick, gray snow clouds darken the sky. Driving through snow in low light can be dangerous.

HIGHLIGHTS

◆ Rain and drizzle are liquid forms of precipitation. Solid precipitation includes snow, sleet, and hail.

◆ Experts define rain as water drops larger than 0.5 mm across, collecting at 1 mm per hour.

◆ A snowflake is made up of many interlaced ice crystals. Its shape reflects the air temperature at the height where it formed.

Clouds

Almost all precipitation develops in clouds. These masses of moisture form in the air where relative humidity exceeds 100 percent, a condition called supersaturation. All clouds eventually unload their moisture as precipitation. The form of precipitation depends on the temperature of the clouds. Warm clouds (above

Rain Shadows

On the windward side of a mountain, air is forced to rise, and so it cools. Cool air can hold less moisture than warm air, so clouds form and rain and snow fall. Settlements on the windward slopes of high mountain ranges receive record levels of precipitation. Cherrapunji, in the Indian Himalayas, gets 1,000 inches (25,000 mm) of rain each year.

By the time the air arrives on the leeward side of the range, it contains little moisture. As the air descends the leeward slope, it warms, which further reduces the chances of rain. Such areas, where little precipitation falls, are known as rain shadows. Calama in Chile lies in the rain shadow of the Andes Mountains. For 400 years, virtually no rain fell there at all. Then on February 10, 1972, torrential rain ended the drought and flooded the town.

Windward side of the mountain

Air cools as it rises, dropping moisture as precipitation

Leeward side of the mountain

Air warms as it descends; there is little precipitation

Rain shadow

Rain shadows occur on a mountain's leeward slope.

freezing point) contain liquid water droplets. Cold clouds (below freezing point) may contain both ice particles and supercooled droplets (water that is still liquid below freezing point).

Even the smallest, lightest water drops or ice particles are heavier than air, so they fall to the ground. However, they fall so slowly—at ⅕ inch (5 mm) per second—that weak rising air currents can keep them aloft. Clouds grow as long as the surrounding air remains supersaturated. Warm clouds produce rain when their droplets become too large and heavy to remain suspended. As they fall, the droplets collide and become larger.

In cold clouds, supercooled droplets and ice particles grow by feeding on moisture in the surrounding air. Once the particles begin to fall, they collide with smaller particles and grow.

Changes in cloud patterns signal that rain or snow is on the way. Frontal systems are responsible for bringing most rain, sleet, and snow. Fronts are the sloping boundaries between large air masses of different temperatures and humidity. Where air masses meet, clouds and precipitation occur.

Fronts are named after the character of the advancing air. Warm fronts bring widespread, persistent rain or snow. Cold fronts may bring heavy precipitation and severe storms.

Rain and drizzle

Rain is the most common form of precipitation. Meteorologists define rain as water drops larger than 0.5 mm across, which collect at 1 mm per hour. Drizzle is made up of drops smaller than light rain. Many people believe that raindrops are shaped like teardrops, but small drops are spherical. Large drops are squat, with flat bottoms and rounded tops, like burger buns.

Snow, sleet, and hail

Snowflakes are collections of many interlaced ice crystals. The shape of each snow crystal depends on the air temperature at the height where it formed. Snowflakes fall slowly, the larger ones at about 3 feet (1 m) per second.

When raindrops fall through an air mass of subzero (below zero) temperatures, they freeze. If the cold air mass is deep enough, the drops freeze as small, solid spheres of clear ice, called sleet. Hailstones are balls of ice that form in violent storms. If they are suspended in the air by rising air currents, they become coated with layer upon layer of ice and grow large and heavy. The largest hailstone ever recorded in the United States fell in Coffeyville, Kansas, on September 3, 1970. It weighed 1 pound 11 ounces (750 g).

CHECK THIS OUT!
✔ATMOSPHERE ✔CLOUD ✔CRYSTAL ✔DROUGHT ✔EVAPORATION AND BOILING ✔FLOOD ✔HUMIDITY ✔ICE ✔METEOROLOGY ✔MONSOON ✔MOUNTAIN ✔NATIONAL WEATHER SERVICE ✔WATER ✔WEATHER

Red Giant

An old star that has grown to be huge and has a relatively cool, red surface

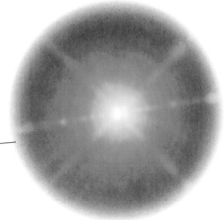

A cluster of ancient stars (left) in the Milky Way, including aging bright red giants (like below).

Toward the end of a star's life, as it uses up the fuel that burns in its core, the star can swell to an enormous size. At the same time, the star's surface temperature drops. Instead of shining bright white or blue, the surface glows a cooler red. This type of star is called a red giant.

How red giants form

Every star generates energy in its core by a process called nuclear fusion. For most of the star's life, fusion converts hydrogen into the heavier element helium and releases energy as electromagnetic radiation. As the radiation blasts out from the core, it pushes up against the rest of the star, keeping the star from collapsing inward. For many millions or even billions of years, this process keeps the star in balance.

As the star uses up the supply of hydrogen in its core, fusion stops. The star keeps shining because radiation takes thousands of years to force its way out to the surface, but with no inner energy source, it eventually begins to shrink.

As the star falls inward, the pressure and temperature in and around its core increase, until the hydrogen around the core gets hot enough to begin to fuse itself. Energy from this fusion heats the layers of gas above it, so while the core continues to shrink, the outer layers of the star expand. The outward pressure from the hydrogen-burning area makes the star expand to many times its former size. When Earth's Sun becomes a red giant (in around 5 billion years), it will swell to 100 times its current diameter, swallowing Venus, Mercury, and perhaps Earth.

The burning hydrogen increases the amount of energy produced by the star. However, because the star's surface area has become much bigger, less energy escapes per square mile of surface than before. The star's surface temperature falls and the light it gives out changes from white-hot to cooler red-hot.

Later stages

A star may go through several red giant stages. As the core shrinks, it gets hot enough to begin the fusion of helium into heavier elements; all heavy elements form in stars this way. The core expands, disrupting the hydrogen-burning area around it, so the star falls inward again. The most massive stars can repeat the process many times, burning heavier and heavier elements. However, the entire red giant phase is only a short part of a star's life, and so red giants are relatively rare.

CHECK THESE OUT!
✔FUSION ✔STAR ✔SUN ✔WHITE DWARF

Refining

A process for removing impurities, particularly from metals

When minerals are taken from the ground, they have all kinds of unwanted material mixed in with them. Most metals, for example, are not found in their pure state in nature. They are usually combined with other elements in ores. Hematite (iron oxide) is an ore of iron. The oxygen has to be removed from this ore to get the pure iron. Obtaining a pure product is called refining. Crude oil, for example, must be refined to provide useful petroleum products. A metal must be refined to remove impurities that can affect the metal's desirable properties.

Impurities can weaken metals or reduce their usefulness. For example, the iron used in steel must be refined to remove phosphorus and sulfur. Phosphorus weakens the steel, and sulfur can make the steel brittle at high temperatures. Copper and aluminum are very useful in electrical equipment because they are good conductors. However, impurities will reduce their ability to conduct electricity.

Refining processes

The processes for refining metals can be divided into two types: those that remove the impurities from the metal, and those that remove the metal, leaving the impurities behind. The oldest method of refining is to use a temperature high enough to melt the metal.

Steel is a very pure form of iron. Nearly all impurities have been removed by refining.

Air is then blown through the molten mixture, or chemicals are added to react with the impurities. A compound containing the impurities is formed. This compound either sinks to the bottom of the mixture or is skimmed off the top.

If the metal has a lower melting point than the impurities, a process called liquation (lih-KWAY-shuhn) can be used. The mix is heated until the metal melts, and it is then poured off, leaving the solid impurities behind.

Some metals, such as mercury and zinc, have very low boiling points. They can be refined by distillation (DIS-tuh-LAY-shuhn). Distillation involves heating a raw material and taking off various materials as they boil. Metals with low boiling points often react readily with oxygen, so the distillation must be carried out without air.

The purest metals are obtained using electricity. The positive plate (anode) is made of the impure metal to be refined. The negative plate (cathode) is made of pure metal. Both plates are dipped in an electrolyte (ih-LEK-truh-LYT; a liquid that conducts electricity), such as molten salt. When a direct current flows through the electrolyte, pure metal collects on the cathode. The impurities either go into solution or are deposited as anode slime. The slime often contains other valuable metal compounds. Pure copper, for example, is obtained by electrolysis, and silver can be recovered from the slime.

Scrap recovery

An important form of refining is the recovery of metals from scrap. More than 40 percent of the world's lead is recovered from compounds in used automobile batteries. The compounds have to be smelted to remove impurities. Tin is recovered from plated cans by electrolysis. This provides pure tin, and the steel scrap left from the cans can be refined by steelmakers. Aluminum beverage cans are refined and reused.

CHECK THESE OUT!
✔ALUMINUM ✔COPPER ✔ELECTROLYSIS ✔METAL
✔METALLURGY ✔ORE ✔SILVER ✔SMELTING

Relativity

A revolutionary theory of physics

Trains that shrink as they whizz past and black holes in space are some of the stranger predictions of a remarkable scientific theory first proposed in the early part of the 20th century. German-born U.S. physicist Albert Einstein's (1879–1955) theory of relativity has helped to explain some of the more mysterious workings of the Universe. Einstein's theory forced scientists to rethink the way objects behave when they travel at very high speeds (close to the speed of light: 186,282 miles or 299,792 km per second). However, relativity has little effect on everyday life. For most purposes, older theories collectively called classical physics (or Newtonian physics) continue to apply.

Relative motion

One of the basic ideas of relativity is that things can appear very different to different observers. Suppose a girl is traveling on a train and a boy is standing by the track watching her go by. The girl then throws a ball toward the front of the train. From her point of view, the ball moves forward at the speed she throws it. From the boy's point of view, the ball moves faster—at the speed of the train plus the speed of the throw.

HIGHLIGHTS

◆ The special theory of relativity deals with the way people experience time and space when they are moving in straight lines at steady speeds.

◆ The general theory of relativity deals with the experience of people in other kinds of relative motion. It helps to explain how gravity works.

◆ Relativity predicts some unusual things. Objects traveling at speeds close to the speed of light seem to shrink in length, and time slows down.

Instead of throwing a ball, suppose the girl shines a flashlight toward the front of the train and measures the speed of the light beam. Remarkably, if the boy measures the speed of the light beam as well, the two measurements will be the same—the train's speed makes no difference.

Special theory of relativity

The idea that the speed of light always has the same value no matter what the position or motion of the observer was Einstein's starting point when he thought up his theory of relativity. The theory is also built around the idea that the same laws of physics must apply to anyone

An artwork showing a black hole. Black holes are thought to bend space and pull in light, according to Einstein's theory.

standing still or moving at a constant speed. When Einstein started to think about these ideas in more detail, he realized that they have some remarkable effects. He tried to imagine himself riding along on a light beam and asked himself what he would see. He came to realize that if the speed of light stays the same, however and from wherever it is measured, other things must change in unusual ways.

One conclusion that Einstein reached almost immediately was that nothing could travel faster than the speed of light. The speed of light is, in effect, the ultimate speed limit for all objects in the Universe. Einstein also showed that when objects move at speeds near to the speed of light, very strange things can happen. Suppose a train is pulled along the track by a locomotive traveling at a speed close to the speed of light. Einstein predicted time would proceed more slowly on the train compared to off it. If a girl took a very long journey on this train and returned to a boy who had been standing by the track when she started out, she would find that he was older than her when she returned.

Relativity also predicts other strange things. If the train shot past the boy at a speed close to the speed of light, the cars of the train would appear to him to be shorter in length. The faster the train traveled, the more the shrinkage. The changes would be noticed only by someone outside the train standing still or moving much slower. To the girl, time would seem to pass normally on the train and it would be the world outside the train that experienced the shrinkage.

Einstein's theory of relativity is actually two separate theories. The predictions described above make up the special theory, so-called

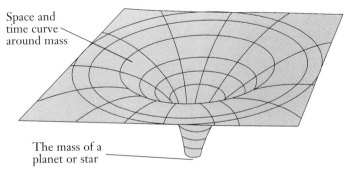

Space and time curve around mass

The mass of a planet or star

Einstein believed that gravity results from space and time being curved by mass.

LOOK CLOSER

Einstein is Proved Right

Einstein's general theory of relativity predicts that a massive body such as a planet or star causes a distortion of space and time around it. Therefore, light must curve toward the body as it passes. In 1919, while the Sun's glare was blocked by the Moon during an eclipse, scientists were able to see how light rays passing near the Sun behaved. They were bent by just the amount predicted by Einstein. This made Einstein's theory world famous.

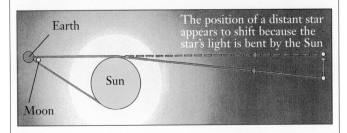

Earth

The position of a distant star appears to shift because the star's light is bent by the Sun

Sun

Moon

Light from a star is bent by the Sun's gravity.

because it works only for observers moving in straight lines at a steady speed (such as the girl traveling on the train).

General theory of relativity

Some time after working out the special theory, Einstein came up with a more complex theory that could deal with other kinds of observer motion. This is called the general theory of relativity. Just as the special theory changed the way scientists thought about objects moving at high speeds, so the general theory revolutionized ideas about gravity. Instead of seeing gravity as a force, Einstein suggested that gravity is a kind of curvature (bending) of space and time that happens near to very massive objects, such as planets. One amazing prediction to come from this theory is the existence of collapsed stars called black holes, which have a gravitational pull so strong that not even light can escape them.

CHECK THESE OUT!
✔BLACK HOLE ✔GRAVITY ✔MOTION
✔NEWTONIAN PHYSICS ✔TIME ✔TIME TRAVEL

Remote Sensing

Gathering data about objects and conditions without being in contact with them

Until the beginning of the 19th century, humans were earthbound. People could only imagine what Earth might look like to a bird flying in the sky or to someone on the Moon. Then came the development of the balloon in the late 18th century, and a century later, the airplane. For the first time, people looked down on Earth's surface. What they saw was restricted to visible light reflected from the surface; it could be obscured by clouds and haze.

Remote sensing is a way of using every part of the electromagnetic spectrum—light, radio waves, microwaves, infrared (heat), ultraviolet, X rays, and gamma rays—to survey Earth and other bodies in the Universe. Scientists are able to view and analyze objects from a great distance by day or night and in all weather conditions.

Detecting by remote sensing

The first major step forward in remote sensing came in 1931. Scientists discovered that dyes could be added to photographic films to make them sensitive to infrared radiation. Infrared photography has since become a valuable tool for scientists, farmers, and the military.

Healthy vegetation reflects infrared, while foliage that has been damaged by human activity, fire, insects, or drought does not. In an aerial photograph, using infrared film, healthy growth appears deep pink, while damaged vegetation appears patchy. Farmers can survey areas where crops are not

thriving, and military observers can spot where soldiers have damaged vegetation to construct camouflaged (hidden) shelters.

Aerial photography remains a part of remote sensing, but other methods have become increasingly important. For example, aerial sensors and scanners aboard aircraft, spacecraft, and satellites collect measurements of energy rather than pictures. Computers analyze the data and produce color-coded digital images.

Many different types of electromagnetic waves can now be used. They provide ways of detecting objects and conditions that would otherwise be hidden. For example, radar waves pass through clouds and desert sand, which block light, but they are reflected by moist soil or rock. If an area is covered

Radar image of Teide volcano on the island of Tenerife in the Canary Islands.

HIGHLIGHTS

◆ Remote sensing uses every part of the electromagnetic spectrum, from radar to X rays.

◆ Sensors and scanners in airplanes, spacecraft, and satellites frequently collect data about the electromagnetic radiation reflected off an object.

◆ Remote sensing is used in agriculture, geology, oceanography, meteorology, and space exploration.

by cloud, recording the energy in a radar scan can provide a digital image of the hidden ground.

Microwaves emitted (given off) from objects or from the atmosphere can give information about their temperature. Infrared scanners can then pinpoint sources of heat. For example, police forces use scanners to find missing injured people, as well as illegal drug-processing facilities and stills (used to make alcoholic drinks). Ultraviolet waves help to detect the presence of ozone (O_3). Both X rays and gamma rays provide data from space, such as the birth of new stars.

Everyday uses

On Earth, remote sensing data can help people to find water, trace weather patterns, make maps, track ocean currents, and calculate the growth of forests. Remote sensing data can save lives by detecting volcanic activity and warning of floods and other severe weather. It can also help with environmental recovery programs. For example, scientists in Canada and the United States have used remote sensing to study soil erosion.

In Ivory Coast, western Africa, remote sensing has been used to find water sources beneath the ground. It has also been used to monitor air pollution. The United States

uses remote sensing along its coasts to learn about changes in the temperature of the surface of the sea, its currents, and its muddiness. This information is used to develop a map of the entire coastal water surface, pinpointing the areas best suited for marine life.

Satellite surveys

There are four main types of Earth survey satellites. Weather satellites provide invaluable information on developing weather systems. Geodetic (JEE-uh-DEH-tik) satellites are used to produce maps. Earth resources satellites provide data on resources including agriculture, forestry, and mineral deposits, and water and marine resources. Finally, there are military reconnaissance (rih-KAH-nuh-SUHNTS) satellites used to survey enemy territory.

The U.S. National Operational Hydrologic Remote Sensing Center uses satellites to measure the gamma rays emitted by traces of radioactive elements in Earth's surface. Snow-covered ground reduces the emissions, so the center can help to predict flooding by snowmelt and the availability of water later in the year. Many industrial and mining companies use data from satellites to identify concentrations of harmful effluents (EH-floo-uhnts; wastes).

Space surveys

Exploration of the planets and stars makes use of gamma rays, X rays, ultraviolet, and infrared radiation. The NASA (National Aeronautics and Space Administration) probe *Clementine* uses remote sensing to study the makeup of Earth and the Moon. The Hubble Space Telescope provides information about other galaxies, star clusters, and the chemical makeup of stars, as well as of planets in the Solar System.

The *Magellan* probe used radar (radio wave echoes) to make a map of Venus. The Infrared Space Observatory of the European Space Agency is designed to find extremely cold stars and to study Titan, Saturn's hazy moon.

CHECK THESE OUT!
✔ELECTROMAGNETIC SPECTRUM
✔HUBBLE SPACE TELESCOPE ✔INFRARED RADIATION
✔RADIO WAVE ✔SATELLITE ✔ULTRAVIOLET RADIATION

River

Natural courses of fresh water that flow mostly downhill across Earth's surface are called rivers. Many rivers start life as mountain springs or are fed by lakes or glaciers. Pulled by gravity, the water flows downhill toward the sea or ocean. Many rivers flow throughout the year. Others, called arroyos (uh-ROY-OHS) in the Americas and wadis (WAH-dees) in Africa and Asia, are dry except when rain falls.

The Nile in Africa is the world's longest river. It flows 4,187 miles (6,700 km) from the equator to the Mediterranean Sea. The Amazon in South America flows for 4,000 miles (6,437 km). It forms the world's largest river system and is over 100 miles (160 km) wide at its mouth.

River systems and erosion

A river is part of a larger drainage system—a pattern of fresh water that drains an area of land. The water collects in small channels (streams or creeks), which join together to form larger channels that eventually form a river. Channels that flow into rivers are called branches or tributaries (TRI-byuh-TER-ees). The Mississippi

HIGHLIGHTS

♦ Rivers carry fine sediment and large rock particles. These materials are called the river's load.

♦ Rivers gradually erode the surface of the land over which they flow. The speed at which erosion takes place depends on the river's volume and speed and the types of rocks on the riverbed.

River drainage system covers 1.2 million square miles (3.1 million sq km), with tributary rivers from two Canadian provinces and 32 U.S. states.

A river's mouth is where the river flows into a larger body of water, such as a lake or an ocean. An estuary (ES-chuh-WER-ee) is where the lower part of a river's course meets the seawater tides, and so it has a mixture of fresh and salt water.

As a river flows toward the sea, it carries with it sediment (rock fragments, clay, silt, or fine sand), called the river's load. Fine sediments are carried along in the water. Coarse sand, pebbles,

Rivers, such as this section of the Yukon in Alaska, drop their load in flat areas, forming islands.

and boulders are dragged along the riverbed. These loads gradually erode (wear away) the riverbed rock to form a channel. The speed of erosion depends on the type of rock, the volume of water, and its speed of flow. A swift-flowing river carries more rocks and sediment than a slow-moving river, eroding the land more quickly.

A river's speed depends on the steepness of the slope over which it flows. Near the beginning, or headwaters, of a river, the slopes are usually steep so the river flows fast and may cut deep gorges or canyons through the landscape. Toward the end of its course, the river flows more slowly through land with more gradual slopes.

Depositing mud and sediment

When the speed of a river slows down, it can no longer carry all of its load, so it deposits (drops) some of its sediment. When the river reaches a plain (flat area), it may shed large quantities of sand, mud, or gravel to form bars. These bars may form a network of shallow, shifting channels in the riverbed. Some rivers drop coarse sand or gravel in fan-shaped deposits called alluvial (uh-LOO-vee-uhl) fans.

When a river floods, it deposits sediment close to its banks. A series of floods may lead to the formation of high banks called natural levees

Rivers flowing over flattish land begin to meander, cutting a loopy path. This is the Wye River in Wales.

(LE-vees). At its mouth, the river may fan out and drop large quantities of fine sediment to form a delta. The world's largest delta lies at the mouth of the Ganges River, in northern India and Bangladesh.

River features

Meanders (mee-AN-duhrs) are natural bends or loops in a river's course that form in flattish land. Swift-flowing water erodes the outside of the bends, while slower-moving water drops sediment on the inside of the curves. Gradually, this process enlarges the meanders and moves them downstream. The river may break through the neck of the loop to form a new course that bypasses the meander. The cut-off loop fills with rainwater to form a pool called an oxbow lake.

Waterfalls occur where a river tumbles over a shelf or cliff of hard rock. Gradually, the water wears away the softer rock below uh hard rock at the base of the cliff. An overhang of the harder rock forms that eventually breaks off, causing the waterfall to slowly move backward upstream.

CHECK THESE OUT!
✔DELTA ✔EROSION ✔OCEAN ✔POLLUTION ✔TIDE

Rock

A rock is a mass of mineral particles. It can contain many different minerals or be made of only one. Pure sandstone usually contains only quartz, whereas granite can contain a mixture of quartz, feldspar, and mica (MY-kuh).

Locked away in a rock is the history of how and where it formed. Geologists try to unravel this story to find out what Earth was like millions of years ago. One of the founding fathers of modern geology was James Hutton (1726–1797) from Scotland. He believed that the rock formations that can be seen today have been occurring in the same way throughout time. Therefore, geologists can explain ancient rocks by looking at the way rocks form today.

Hot rocks

There are three broad groups of rocks: igneous, sedimentary, and metamorphic. Igneous rocks are made from magma (liquid rock) or lava (magma that reaches Earth's surface). As magma gradually cools, deep in Earth's crust, mineral crystals begin to form. Slowly, often over millions of years, crystals develop and eventually a solid rock is made. These igneous rocks are called intrusive rocks because they intrude (invade) other rocks in the crust. The magma seeps into cracks in the crust and surrounds other rocks, melting them. They become part of the magma. Granite and gabbro are two igneous rocks that form in this way, and they may form in masses many miles across.

A huge granite boulder in Australia, one of many known as the Devil's Marbles.

HIGHLIGHTS

◆ There are three main groups of rocks: igneous, sedimentary, and metamorphic.

◆ More than 95 percent of the rocks in Earth's crust are made of silicon compounds.

Lava reaches temperatures of 1832°F (1000°C) and flows across the land with devastating results. When lava cools, it too produces igneous rocks. These are called extrusive rocks and include basalt and rhyolite (RY-uh-lyt).

Squashed layers

Sedimentary rocks are formed from the particles of other rocks broken

off by weathering and erosion. Pebbles, sand, and other fragments are carried by rivers, wind, and glaciers and deposited on the seabed. Strata (layers) form, which, over millions of years, are squashed by more layers and form sedimentary rocks such as sandstone and limestone.

Metamorphic (changing form) rocks include marble, gneiss (NYS), and slate. They form when other rocks are changed by being squeezed and heated inside Earth's crust. This often occurs during mountain building. When part of Earth's crust moves below or into another, great pressure and heat is generated and rocks are changed into metamorphic rocks.

Rock minerals

Nearly 3,000 minerals have been named and described, but very few of them are important rock-formers. Many of the rock-formers contain the elements silicon and oxygen and are called silicates. Some of these minerals are relatively pale colored and have a low specific gravity, around 2.6. Specific gravity is a measure of how heavy (or light) a mineral is compared with water. Minerals with a low specific gravity include quartz, feldspar, and muscovite mica. Another group is heavier (with a specific gravity of 3.0 or higher) and dark colored. This includes the amphibole (AM-fuh-BOHL), pyroxene (py-RAHK-seen), and olivine (AH-luh-VEEN) mineral families, and biotite mica.

Feldspars are hard minerals that can be broken down to make clay. They make up more than half of Earth's crust and are common in most igneous rocks, many metamorphic rocks, and some sediments. Quartz is harder than feldspar and does not wear down easily. For this reason, it makes up many sedimentary rocks such as sandstone. Quartz is also common in granite and metamorphic rocks, such as gneiss.

The silicate mineral mica is soft and flakes easily because its atoms are arranged in sheets. It has a silvery sheen and is often found in granite and the metamorphic rock schist (SHIST). Amphiboles and pyroxenes are a group of complex silicate minerals. They are dark green or black and occur in many igneous and metamorphic rocks. Calcite, which is the main part of limestone, often comes from living

things. Organisms such as mollusks take in calcite from seawater. When they die, their shells build up to form limestone.

LOOK CLOSER

The Rock Cycle

Geologists consider that rocks are all related in a cycle. The first to be formed are igneous rocks when magma cools in Earth's crust (Earth's outer layer above the mantle) to make rocks such as granite and basalt. When they have been pushed up through Earth's crust into mountains, they can be weathered and eroded, and small particles break off to be carried in rivers to the sea. Here, the fragments from the original igneous rocks are deposited as layers of sediment. In time, these layers harden to become sedimentary rock such as sandstone.

Earth's crust is constantly moving and, in time, these sedimentary strata may be dragged deep underground. Here they are heated, squeezed, and changed into metamorphic rocks such as slate. As the plate movement continues, these metamorphic rocks can go deeper underground, where they melt and change into magma. The rock cycle then starts again as new igneous rocks form.

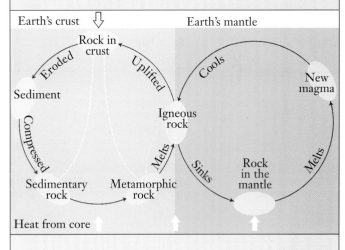

Rock on Earth is formed and re-formed in a cycle.

CHECK THESE OUT!

✔CLAY ✔EARTH ✔GEOLOGY ✔IGNEOUS ROCK
✔LANDFORM ✔LIMESTONE ✔MAGMA
✔METAMORPHIC ROCK ✔MINERALOGY
✔PLATE TECTONICS ✔QUARTZ ✔SEDIMENTARY ROCK

Russian Space Mission

Space exploration programs carried out by the Soviet Union and then Russia

During the second half of the 20th century, the United States and the former Soviet Union (Russia and her neighboring states) battled to outdo one another in what was called the space race. Although the United States scored some spectacular successes by putting the first man on the Moon and pioneering the reusable space shuttle, the Soviet Union also achieved some notable firsts. These included putting the first man and woman into space and making the first unpiloted flights to the Moon.

The early missions

The space age began on October 4, 1957, when Russian scientists launched an artificial satellite called *Sputnik 1*. It carried no crew, only a radio transmitter that sent signals back to Earth. One month later, the Russians launched their next satellite, *Sputnik 2*. Further Sputnik missions managed to return to Earth in one piece, which led to the development of crewed spaceflight.

Russia's next milestone was the launch on April 12, 1961, of the world's first crewed space flight carrying astronaut Yuri Gagarin (1934–1968). His spacecraft, *Vostok 1*, looked nothing like today's rockets. It was about 16 feet (4.9 m) high and had a ball-shaped capsule with a cone-shaped nose. Later Vostok flights saw the launch of Valentina Tereshkova, the first woman in space, the first three-person space crew, and the first walk in space. In 1967, new sets of missions named Soyuz and Salyut were begun. Launched in April 1971, *Salyut 1* was the world's first piloted space station.

The Russian space station **Salyut 7** *in orbit. Spacecraft* **Soyuz T14** *(launched in 1985) can be seen attached to the bottom of the station.*

HIGHLIGHTS

◆ Yuri Gagarin became the first person to travel in space on April 12, 1961.

◆ The Soviet Vostok program included the first space flight by a woman, Valentina Tereshkova.

◆ The first piloted space station, *Salyut 1*, was launched by Soviet scientists in 1971.

◆ Soviet spacecraft made the first missions to the Moon, Venus, and Mars.

Moon missions

During the 1960s, the United States and the Soviet Union raced to put cosmonauts (the Russian word for astronauts) on the Moon. The Americans won that particular race in 1969, but only by a whisker. For a time in 1968, a Russian space program called Zond seemed set to place cosmonauts on the Moon ahead of the Apollo astronauts. Last-minute problems meant that the Zond mission was delayed and, rather than come second to the United States, the Soviet Union decided to give up its attempt.

Soviet spacecraft nevertheless made many important missions to the Moon between 1959 and 1976. A series of Soviet missions called Luna included the first flight past the Moon and the first soft landing on the Moon's surface. The *Luna 9* craft, launched on January 31, 1966, transmitted back to Earth the first video footage of the Moon's surface. Another Luna craft returned the first samples of Moon rock. Each of these events was an important achievement.

Venus and Mars missions

As long ago as 1961, Sputnik rockets were launched for Venus. After several unsuccessful attempts, *Venera 4* finally parachuted into Venus's atmosphere on October 18, 1967. It managed to transmit back to Earth important information about Venus before being destroyed by the high pressure of Venus's atmosphere. Later Venera probes, and craft launched in the 1970s and 1980s called Vega, carried sophisticated scientific equipment including radar sets and temperature gauges. They transmitted photographs, video footage, and measurements of Venus's climate.

Conquering Mars remains one of the greatest challenges of space exploration. Soviet missions have played an important part in exploring this mysterious planet during the last 40 years. Although the first Soviet Mars probes were launched in the early 1960s, it was not until 1971 that a probe called *Mars 3* finally landed on the planet's surface. Its onboard transmitter failed soon after touchdown, however, so very little information was received. Later Mars probes also met with technical difficulties, some flying past the planet completely and others failing to send back to Earth any useful information. However, a probe called *Mars 5* did land and transmit back much useful information about the surface and atmosphere of Mars.

CHECK THESE OUT!
✔APOLLO MISSION ✔LUNAR MISSION ✔MERCURY MISSION ✔NASA ✔VIKING PROBE ✔VOYAGER PROBE

EVERYDAY SCIENCE

Cosmonaut Yuri Gagarin was the first person in space. His flight lasted one and a half hours.

Russian Space Firsts

Russian space missions have included some notable firsts. Yuri Alekseyevich Gagarin (1934–1968) became the first human in space when he circled Earth in the *Vostok 1* craft on April 12, 1961. He became an international hero, but he never again ventured into space. He was killed while piloting a fighter jet in March 1968.

The Soviet Union also put the first woman into space. Valentina Tereshkova's historic mission took place on June 16, 1963, when she took part in a three-day flight on *Vostok 6*. This important mission studied the effects of weightlessness on cosmonauts, including the differences between men and women.

Soviet cosmonaut Alexei Leonov made history again when he completed the very first space walk on March 18, 1965. Leonov's walk lasted 12 minutes, but it took him another 8 minutes to return inside the capsule when he found that his inflated spacesuit was too big for him to fit back through the hatch.

Salts

Compounds formed by an acid and a base reacting together

In everyday language, the word *salt* usually refers to the white substance used in cooking or sprinkled on food. To a scientist, salt is used to describe a large group of chemical substances, which includes common or table salt. Plaster of Paris, gunpowder, chalk, washing soda,

HIGHLIGHTS

◆ Salts are formed when the positive ions of a base combine with the negative ions of an acid, or when a metal reacts with an acid.

◆ Many acids and bases combine to form a salt and water. When solid, salts usually form crystals.

◆ About 3.5 percent of the weight of seawater is due to dissolved salts.

Common salt (NaCl) is an essential part of the human diet. Like all salts, it is formed by the reaction of an acid and a base.

bicarbonate of soda, Epsom salts, paint pigments, and fertilizers are just a few examples of salts. About 3.5 percent of the weight of seawater is due to dissolved salts, including mainly sodium chloride (common salt), but also smaller amounts of magnesium sulfate, calcium sulfate, magnesium bromide, and potassium chloride.

Acids and bases

Any substance that dissolves in water can be tested with indicator or pH paper and put into one of three groups: acid, base, or neutral. If the pH is less than 7, the substance is an acid; if the pH is greater than 7, the substance is a base. If the pH is equal to 7, the substance is neutral. Bases are the opposite of acids. When acids and bases are mixed in the correct amounts, they neutralize each other to produce a salt and water.

All acids, bases, and salts are made of ions (EYE-uhns; charged particles). An acid, base, or salt is made of positive and negative ions, which can attract one another. However, dissolving such substances in water frees the ions from each other. All acids form positive hydrogen ions when they dissolve in water. The negative ions formed when bases dissolve in water are often hydroxide ions. The positive ions in a base are varied, but are often a metal such as sodium, calcium, or potassium.

When an acid and a base neutralize each other, the hydrogen ions from the acid combine with the hydroxide ions from the base to form water molecules. The positive ions from the base and the negative ions from the acid are then left in the water as a salt. When the water evaporates, the positive and negative ions bond together to form crystals of the salt:

acid + base → salt + water

If the acid is hydrochloric acid and the base is sodium hydroxide, the new salt produced when neutralization takes place is sodium chloride (also called common salt or table salt).

Metals and acids

When some metals react with acids, hydrogen gas is given off and the salt ions form a solution. If this solution evaporates, a salt is left. Magnesium, for example, reacts with dilute sulfuric acid to form a solution of magnesium sulfate (or Epsom salts) plus hydrogen gas. Not all salts can be made by using a metal to displace hydrogen from an acid. There is no reaction at all when some metals are added to a dilute acid. By contrast, it is very dangerous to add a very reactive metal to an acid.

Crystals of sodium chloride (common salt) are cubic.

LOOK CLOSER

Hard Water

In some places, tap water lathers easily with soap. In this case, the water is "soft." In other places, the same amount of soap and water forms a scum and hardly any lather. This is a sign that the water is "hard." Hard water can be a problem in pipes, kettles, and heating systems, where it forms a solid fur (limescale), which does not conduct heat as well as the pure metal. Hardness in water is caused by dissolved magnesium and calcium salts, which are not removed at the waterworks. Some hard water has a salt called calcium hydrogen carbonate in it. When the water is boiled, the calcium hydrogen carbonate decomposes to calcium carbonate (chalk). Chalk is insoluble and collects on the sides of the kettle or pipes as fur. Hardness caused by calcium hydrogen carbonate is called temporary hardness because it is removed by boiling the water.

Other types of hard water contain calcium or magnesium sulfates. These salts are unaffected by boiling, and so cause permanent water hardness, which can, however, be removed by a water softener.

The problem of scum is less serious today because modern detergents (used to clean clothes and dishes and in most shampoos) clean like soap but do not form a scum or scale with hard water.

Naming salts

Most salts are made of metal ions and acidic ions. The crystals of each salt have a particular shape. The name of a salt reveals the metal ions and acidic ions from which it was made. Salts formed from sulfuric acid are called sulfates; salts formed from hydrochloric acid are called chlorides; and salts formed from nitric acid are called nitrates.

A salt whose acid name ends in -ide has an acid containing only one element. For example, sodium chloride is made only of the elements sodium and chlorine. An -ate ending reveals that the salt also contains oxygen. Sodium sulfate, for example, is made of sodium, sulfur, and oxygen.

CHECK THESE OUT!
✔ACID AND BASE ✔CHEMICAL REACTION
✔CRYSTAL ✔ION ✔WATER

Sand

Grainy material made up of small fragments of weathered rocks or shells

Sand is made up of fragments of rock or shell. These fragments are formed by weathering (the action of wind and chemicals). Sand forms nearly 2 percent of Earth's crust and is found mainly in two very different environments on Earth—the seashore and the desert.

Sand mixtures

Pure sands are made up of one material, such as quartz or coral fragments. Most sands, however, are a mixture of materials. On average, sand contains 65 percent quartz, 15 percent feldspar, 15 percent rock fragments, and 5 percent clay, with small amounts of other materials.

Sand particles range in size from 0.06 to 2 mm across. They are defined as particles that are smaller than gravel but larger than silt. Sand grains may be either angular or have a more rounded shape. Generally, newly weathered rock fragments have sharp corners. They become rounded over time as the corners are worn down by erosion.

Sand ripples in the Namib Desert, southwest Africa, formed by the wind. Waves form the same ripples on a sandy beach.

HIGHLIGHTS

◆ Sand is made up of small rocks or shell particles. These fragments are light enough to be carried along by powerful water currents or strong winds.

◆ Sand is found in rivers, deserts, coasts, and on the ocean floor. These areas are characterized by powerful currents of moving air or water.

◆ Sandstone is a sedimentary rock.

Where sand is found

Sand is found in rivers, desert dunes, along sea coasts, and on the seabed. All of these places have powerful currents of moving air or water. Grains of sand are larger than particles of silt or clay, but they can be suspended and carried along by powerful water currents and high winds.

Large areas of sand are found only where there is a plentiful supply of sediment and strong winds or water currents. Where wind or current strength drops, the particles are deposited. The largest and heaviest grains are dropped first.

Sand often forms wave patterns when moved by wind or water. Sand waves vary from small ripples on a riverbed to giant dunes in deserts.

Sand waves form when an eddy (a current of air or water moving against the general flow) or obstruction causes the current to slow and deposit sand. Once a small mound is formed, this obstructs the current and other mounds develop in a wavelike pattern. Desert dunes move gradually downwind as sand is pushed up the windward side of the dune and cascades down the sheltered side.

Bars, beds, and banks

Sand is a feature of many rivers. It collects to form bars on riverbanks or in midstream. Point bars are found in meandering (winding) rivers such as the Mississippi River. The deposits form on the inside of bends when the river has flooded and then subsided. Midchannel bars form where sand builds up around obstacles. Much of the sand in rivers is eventually carried downstream to form a delta at the river's mouth.

Deserts and dunes

More than 99 percent of the windblown sand on Earth is found in deserts. Sand dunes are a feature of some desert landscapes, for example in north Africa, Namibia, Arabia, and Australia, but they are uncommon. They form in areas where there is plenty of sand, strong winds, and little soil to bind the surface sediment together.

There are two main types of sand dunes. Seif (SEEF) dunes are long, straight ridges of sand that usually form in the direction of the prevailing wind. Barchan (BAHR-KAHN) dunes are crescent-shaped, with crescent "tails" stretching away in the direction of the wind.

Coastlines

Sandy beaches are rare, considering the length of coastline on Earth. For a beach to develop, there must be an abundant supply of sand. The sediment is moved along the coast by longshore drift, which occurs when waves strike the shore at an angle. Sand is deposited to form a beach where water currents are weak, for example, in coves (sheltered inlets). Large deposits of sand offshore form barrier beaches, which create lagoons of quiet water. Most of Earth's sand is carried out to sea and ends up on the seabed.

CHECK THIS OUT!
✔COAST ✔DELTA ✔DESERT ✔EROSION ✔OCEAN
✔QUARTZ ✔SEDIMENTARY ROCK

LOOK CLOSER

Sandstone and Silicon

Sandstone is a sedimentary rock formed of compacted (tightly pressed together) sand particles. The sand grains become cemented together when they are buried under new layers of sediment. Sandstone rocks generally resist erosion well, so they often form prominent features in the landscape. They are common in mountain regions, such as the Appalachians in North America and the Apennines in Italy.

Sand and sandstones exist in a wide range of colors, including black, brown, green, red, white, and yellow. The color of the sand or rock depends on the minerals, often only in small quantities, in the sand. For example, hematite (iron oxide) and limonite (hydrated iron oxide) make sand yellow, while glauconite (a silicate mineral) makes sand green. Oxidation can also affect the color.

Silicon is found combined with other elements in sand and sandstone. Silicon is a semiconductor widely used in the manufacture of computer chips. Compounds of silicon are also very useful. Silica (silicon dioxide; SiO_2) is used to produce glass and as a raw material in the manufacture of ceramics. Silicon carbide (SiC) is made by fusing carbon and silica. It is almost as hard as diamond, and it is widely used in manufacturing as an abrasive (uh-BRAY-siv; a substance used for smoothing).

A prominent sandstone formation near Page in Arizona. Sandstone is hard and resists erosion.

Satellite

An object that moves through space around a larger body, usually a planet

A satellite is any object held in orbit around another, more massive object by the pull of gravity. The planets are technically satellites of the Sun, but the term is usually used to refer to a body orbiting a planet. This may be a natural moon or a manufactured vehicle.

Satellites obey laws of motion first discovered by German astronomer Johannes Kepler (1571–1630) in the early 1600s—they orbit in an ellipse (a stretched circle) around their parent planet. Satellites are kept in orbit by gravity. If gravity did not exist, then they would simply fly out of orbit and keep going in a straight line. Gravity constantly pulls a satellite back toward the planet, canceling out this tendency to shoot away into space, and keeping it in an orbit above the planet's curving surface.

Natural satellites

Natural satellites of the planets in Earth's Solar System are called moons (because Earth's main satellite is called the Moon). Most moons formed at the same time as the planets (about 4.6 billion years ago) and from the same gas, ice, and dust particles. Some formed elsewhere in the Solar System and were later captured when they strayed too close to the planets. A few moons have strange orbits or other features that indicate they were captured by their planet's gravity.

The largest moons in the Solar System, such as Jupiter's Ganymede and Saturn's Titan, are larger than the planet Mercury, while the smallest, such as the shepherd moons within Saturn's rings, are only tens of miles across. The size of a moon affects its shape. Larger moons have stronger gravity, and so pulled themselves into spheres (balls) as they formed. Small moons with weak gravity may have odd, uneven shapes.

The composition of a moon depends on the region of the Solar System where it formed. The moons of planets close to the Sun are rocky. Earth's Moon has a similar composition to Earth itself, while Phobos and Deimos, the satellites of Mars, are probably captured asteroids. Farther out, Jupiter's largest moons, Io, Europa, Ganymede, and Callisto, are a mixture of rock and ice, while Saturn's moons are almost entirely icy. These differences occur because larger amounts of ice survived farther from the heat of the Sun, while closer in, the ice evaporated.

Most moons orbit above their planet's equator (ih-KWAY-tuhr; imaginary line around a planet at equal distances from its poles) and rotate in the same direction as the planet itself. Over millions of years, the gravitational pull of a planet on a moon slows the moon's rotation until it is locked with one side facing its planet.

Most moons are too small to hold on to an atmosphere or to trap heat inside them to fuel geological activity, but there are exceptions. The closest moons to Jupiter and Saturn are heated by the tug of each huge planet's gravity, allowing volcanoes, shifting tectonic plates, and even liquid water to exist on these moons. Titan's low temperature and high mass even allow it to hold on to an atmosphere of nitrogen and methane (gases present in Earth's atmosphere).

Artificial satellites

Most artificial (humanmade) satellites orbit Earth, although a few have now been put in orbit around other planets. Over 4,500 satellites have

---

HIGHLIGHTS

◆ All satellites are held in elliptical orbits by the pull of gravity from a larger body.

◆ Most natural satellites formed billions of years ago from the same cloud of gas, ice, and dust that formed their parent planet.

◆ Artificial satellites can be put into a wide range of different orbits depending on their job.

◆ Artificial satellites can be used for space science, astronomy, weather observation, remote sensing, communications, or military purposes.

been put into orbit since 1957, and many are still in space, although only a few hundred are still in use. In order to put a satellite into orbit, a rocket-powered launch vehicle must be used to overcome Earth's gravitational pull and give the satellite enough speed to stay in orbit without falling back to Earth. Satellites must orbit at about 100 miles (160 km) above the Earth to avoid drag from the atmosphere. They often have engines so that they can change their position.

Satellites can occupy a variety of orbits. Many are put into Low Earth Orbit (LEO), less than a thousand miles above the Earth. In LEO, satellites circle the Earth in a few hours and have a good view of Earth. It is also relatively easy to reach this altitude (height above ground), and some satellites can even be recovered for maintenance (this is the operating orbit for space shuttles and space stations).

Polar orbits are LEOs that pass over or close to Earth's poles, rather than orbiting above the

Pictures taken from the space probe **Voyager 2** *showing Neptune (blue) from the surface of its moon, Triton (gray).*

equator. Polar orbits have an important advantage. Because the Earth is rotating below the satellite, the satellite can observe large areas of the Earth's surface during its orbit. Polar orbit is often used for remote sensing satellites, which study Earth from space.

Elliptical orbits bring a satellite close to Earth on one side, and take it far out into space on the other. Because the satellite slows down as it gets farther out, it can keep one hemisphere of Earth in view for a long time. This is useful for weather and communications satellites.

Elliptical orbits are also used to transfer satellites to higher circular orbits—especially to the geostationary orbit 22,300 miles (35,900 km) above Earth's equator. In this orbit, a satellite takes precisely one day to circle Earth, so its view of Earth never changes. This is useful for some weather satellites, but most important for communications satellites. A geostationary satellite seems to hang at one point in the sky as seen from Earth. It can be used as a fixed platform for bouncing radio signals between opposite sides of the Earth.

CHECK THESE OUT!
✔MASS ✔MECHANICS ✔MOON ✔REMOTE SENSING
✔SOLAR SYSTEM ✔SPACE STATION

LOOK CLOSER

Sputnik 1

The first artificial satellite was *Sputnik 1*, launched by the Soviet Union on October 4, 1957. *Sputnik 1* was a steel ball 23 inches (58 cm) wide, weighing 184 pounds (83 kg). It is shown (right) with its parts separated. *Sputnik 1* was equipped with a simple radio transmitter to send a signal back to Earth. *Sputnik 1* was launched into an orbit 150 to 580 miles (242 to 934 km) above Earth and remained in orbit until 1958, when it fell back into Earth's atmosphere.

Saturn

The second largest planet in the Solar System after Jupiter

Saturn is the sixth planet from the Sun and was the most distant known before the invention of the telescope. The planet has an enormous family of at least 18 satellites, including Titan, which has a thick atmosphere. Saturn is most famous for its spectacular rings.

Giant planet

Saturn is a giant planet with a diameter of 75,000 miles (120,000 km), which makes it nine times wider than the Earth, and only a few thousand miles smaller than Jupiter. It orbits the Sun at a distance of 860 million miles (1.4 billion km), taking 29.5 years to complete one orbit. The earliest records of Saturn come from ancient Assyria (modern Turkey and Iraq) in the 7th century B.C.E., but it has probably been known since prehistoric times.

Because Saturn is so far away, little was known of it until the invention of the telescope, and most knowledge of the planet today comes from the space probes *Voyagers 1* and *2*. With the naked eye, the planet appears as a reasonably bright yellow-white star. A telescope shows the rings and the light and dark bands across the planet's surface. The view of the planet from Earth is constantly changing as a result of Saturn's orbit.

HIGHLIGHTS

◆ Saturn's rings are made of billions of boulder-sized blocks of ice, each in a separate orbit.

◆ The ring particles were probably created by the breakup of a moon.

◆ Saturn's moons are made largely from ice. Some show signs of geological activity.

◆ The largest moon, Titan, has a thick orange atmosphere. It is probably made of ice coated with sticky oils and tars.

Made of gas

Like Jupiter, Uranus, and Neptune, Saturn is a gas giant planet. Although it is huge, it is a ball of light gases—mostly hydrogen and helium. Saturn has a lower density than water, so it would float in a large enough ocean. Saturn's outer layer of clouds has muted colors compared to the bright reds and blues of Jupiter. The clouds show up only as light or dark patches. This is because the entire planet is shrouded in a haze of ammonia ice crystals. Below this haze, the colors are probably similar to Jupiter's red and blue swirls.

Saturn spins rapidly, rotating in 10 hours and 30 minutes. This means that the planet has difficulty holding itself together and so bulges around the equator. It rotates more slowly at its poles and more rapidly at its equator.

Under the clouds

Below the clouds, the planet is much calmer and rotates as if it were a solid object. Within a few hundred miles of the surface, the pressures are so great that hydrogen condenses from a gas into a liquid. Farther into the planet, the hydrogen molecules are broken up to create a sea of electrically charged liquid hydrogen. At the planet's center is a rocky core, about the size of Earth. The planet's gravity is slowly causing these inner layers to contract, building up pressure and releasing heat, which drives the weather in the planet's huge atmosphere. Saturn has the highest wind speeds in the Solar System, exceeding 1,100 miles per hour (1,600 km/h). In all, Saturn releases twice as much heat as it receives from the Sun.

LOOK CLOSER

Saturn's Moons

Saturn has a huge family of moons—at least 18. Closest to the planet are the tiny shepherd satellites, which orbit inside the rings and help to keep some of the narrow ringlets in place. Farther out are icy worlds, such as Mimas and Enceladus, Tethys, Dione, and Rhea.

The largest moon, Titan, is shrouded in a thick orange atmosphere of nitrogen and helium. In 2004, a space probe called Huygens (named for the 17th-century Dutch astronomer who first spotted Saturn's rings) will drop into the atmosphere and investigate Titan's surface. Astronomers think it is made of ice, but it may be covered in sticky oils and explosive gases. Titan would be extremely inhospitable to life. Its surface temperature is around –290°F (–180°C).

Beyond Titan lie tiny Hyperion and the mysterious Iapetus, a satellite with one bright half and one dark half, which changes its brightness depending on where it is in its orbit when it is seen from Earth. It is probably flying into some kind of dark material as it moves around its orbit.

Saturn's outermost satellite, Phoebe, is probably a captured asteroid. It orbits Saturn in the opposite direction from all the other moons. Phoebe also has a very dark surface, and it may be the source of the unknown material coating one half of Iapetus.

A photo of Saturn taken at a distance of 20 million miles by **Voyager 2.**

The rings

Saturn's rings are magnificent. The first people who used telescopes to look at the planet noticed its odd shape, but it was many years before Dutch astronomer Christiaan Huygens (1629–1695) realized there was a ring around the planet. From Earth, the rings look flat and solid. By the 19th century, astronomers knew that the rings could not be solid and must be made up of tiny particles, each in its own orbit around Saturn. In the 1980s, the *Voyager* space probes revealed the rings' full complexity.

The brightest rings are 171,000 miles (275,000 km) across, but just half a mile (1 km) deep. A close-up view shows they are divided into thousands of narrow ringlets. The rings are made of chunks of ice ranging from boulders to house-sized blocks, all orbiting within a region around Saturn where the planet's gravity stops large moons forming. Saturn is constantly pulling material out of the rings, so they cannot have lasted since the planet's formation billions of years ago. Astronomers think they may be the result of a recent collision between two moons.

CHECK THESE OUT!

✔ASTEROID ✔JUPITER ✔NEPTUNE ✔SATELLITE ✔SOLAR SYSTEM ✔TELESCOPE ✔URANUS ✔VOYAGER PROBE

Saturn's rings seen from **Voyager 2** *in 1981. The rings are made up of particles in individual orbit.*

Season

A season is a time of year associated with a particular weather pattern. In many parts of the world, the seasons greatly affect temperatures, day lengths, and vegetation. In these ways, seasons influence farming practices, the clothes people wear, and all outdoor life.

Temperate parts of the world experience four seasons: spring, summer, fall, and winter. In many areas, winter is associated with snow, spring with rain, summer with heat, and fall with the bright colors of dying leaves. Other parts of the world have different seasons. The polar regions experience very variable conditions throughout the year, but only two major seasons. Spring and fall are barely noticeable. Winters are long and bitterly cold, and summers are brief.

Tropical regions experience less variation in day length and temperature. Various parts of the tropics have different climates. Some areas experience only one season. Other parts have a wet and a dry season, or even two wet and two dry seasons each year.

In the Northern Hemisphere, the seasons are defined astronomically as spring (March 21 to June 21), summer (June 21 to September 22), fall (September 22 to December 21), and winter (December 21 to March 21). Traditionally, these

Temperate regions have four distinct seasons. In the fall, deciduous leaves turn red-gold as they die.

HIGHLIGHTS

◆ Temperatures, rainfall, and day lengths can vary greatly with the seasons.

◆ The seasons occur because Earth is tilted on its axis. At any time of year, one hemisphere tilts toward the Sun, while the other tilts away.

◆ Temperate regions experience four seasons: spring, summer, fall, and winter. Polar regions have only summer and winter.

◆ Tropical regions have the least seasonal variation.

seasons are linked to the farming year. Spring is the sowing season, and summer is the growing season. Crops are harvested in fall, and winter is the dormant (resting) season. In the Southern Hemisphere, the seasons are reversed (summer lasts from December 21 to March 21, and so on).

Causes of the seasons

The seasons occur because Earth tilts on its axis, at an angle of 23.5 degrees, as it moves around the Sun. During the Northern Hemisphere's summer, the North Pole tilts toward the Sun. During winter it tilts away.

Earth's tilt affects the area of its surface that is bathed in sunlight, and the angle at which the Sun's rays hit the atmosphere. In turn, these affect how long the days last and the intensity of sunlight. In June, the Northern Hemisphere experiences more direct sunlight, longer hours of daylight, and warmer temperatures because it is tilted toward the Sun. In winter, it tilts away, which causes shorter days and cooler weather.

Seasonal changes in sunlight

The polar regions experience dramatic seasonal variation in the length of days and nights. In the Arctic on June 21, the Sun never sinks below the horizon, so it is light for 24 hours a day. On the same date, the Sun never rises in the Antarctic. The situation is reversed on December 21.

Despite these dramatic changes, the polar regions experience less seasonal variation in temperature than might be expected. This is because the Sun's rays always strike Earth's surface at a pronounced slant near the poles. Therefore, the rays have farther to travel through Earth's atmosphere, which reduces their warmth. The poles remain cold throughout the year, though are warmer in summer than winter.

The world's temperate regions also experience considerable variation in day length and temperature according to the seasons. During summer, the days are long and the sunlight is hotter because the Sun is more directly overhead.

In tropical regions, the midday Sun is roughly overhead throughout the year. The Sun's rays have only a short distance to travel through the atmosphere, so they are very hot. Temperatures are always warm, and the days and nights are always about the same length.

The seasons also change the balance of gases in Earth's atmosphere. The amount of water vapor in the air varies with the seasons, as do ozone and carbon dioxide levels.

Seasonal rainfall patterns

Sleet, snow, hail, and rainfall also vary by season in many parts of the world. Local patterns of rainfall occur yearly, thanks to seasonal movements of air and winds. Other regions experience slight seasonal variation, including rainy areas such as Britain, and dry regions, such

---

LOOK CLOSER

Solstices and Equinoxes

The longest and shortest days of the year are called solstices. The Sun appears highest overhead at noon on the summer solstice, the longest day of the year. It appears lowest overhead at noon on the winter solstice, the shortest day. In the Northern Hemisphere, the summer solstice falls around June 21, and the winter solstice around December 21. The solstices are reversed in the Southern Hemisphere. Two equinoxes occur midway between the solstices, in spring and fall. On the spring equinox (March 21) and the autumn equinox (September 22), the days and nights last for about 12 hours each everywhere on Earth.

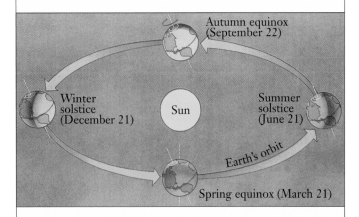

Diagram showing how Earth's orbit is divided into four seasons in the Northern Hemisphere.

---

as the Sahara Desert in north Africa. In the tropics and subtropics, rainfall tends to be heavier in summer. Around the equator (imaginary line around the Earth at equal distances from the poles), a narrow belt of heavy rainfall moves north and south with the seasons. Some parts of the tropics, such as south Asia, experience seasonal winds called monsoons that bring very heavy rain.

CHECK THESE OUT!
✔CLIMATE ✔EARTH ✔EQUINOX AND SOLSTICE
✔MONSOON ✔RAIN, SLEET, AND SNOW ✔SUN
✔TROPICAL REGION ✔WEATHER

Sedimentary Rock

Rock made from sediment squeezed together in layers

Much of Earth's surface is covered in a thin layer of sediment. Sediment is made up of dust, small stones, and other bits of material that were once part of larger objects. Sedimentary rock forms when this material lithifies (LIH-thuh-FYS; changes to stone). This mainly occurs deep in Earth's crust, although some limestones lithify under only a few meters of other rock. In these situations, water is squeezed out of the sediment and new chemicals are mixed in. These fill the tiny pores (spaces) and help to cement the fragments into a rock.

Sedimentary rock characteristics

The most characteristic feature of sedimentary rock, which helps to tell it apart from igneous and metamorphic rock, is its layering. Geologists (scientists who study the history and structure of rocks) call the layers strata (STRAH-tuh). Each layer (stratum) was once the bed of an ancient sea or lake. These layers often contain fossils,

HIGHLIGHTS

◆ Sedimentary rocks are made of fragments of other rocks and from the remains of living organisms.

◆ Sediments can be transported by rivers, the wind, glaciers, and ocean currents.

◆ Deposited sediments are compressed and cemented by chemicals to form solid rocks.

which are the preserved remains of organisms that lived around the time the sediment was formed. By studying the features of the rock and any fossils it may contain, a geologist can tell in what sort of environment the rock formed and how many millions of years old it is.

Many sedimentary rocks are of great economic importance. They are used widely in the building industry. Some contain oil and gas deposits, valuable minerals such as iron ore, and some may also contain underground water supplies.

These rocks are divided into three

Sedimentary rock made up of layers of red sandstone in Arizona. Erosion has smoothed the rock face.

main groups (detrital, biogenic, and chemical) according to how they have been created. In each group there are many different types of rock.

Detrital rocks

Detritus (dih-TRY-tuhs) is the mass of fragments of rock, including sand, pebbles, and mud that lies on Earth's surface. Detrital rocks are made from these materials. Rock fragments are caused by weathering or erosion.

Weathering involves chemical changes taking place in the rocks. When rainwater (a weak acid) falls on rocks such as limestone, it changes the calcite in the limestone into calcium bicarbonate, which is easily dissolved in water and carried away. Acidic rainwater also attacks feldspar (a mineral in granite) and turns it into clay. In cold climates, ice fills cracks in the rocks and expands them, causing fragments to break off. Water in the pores or joints in a rock will freeze and expand, causing the rock to break into grains of sediment. Erosion is caused by running water breaking off pieces of rock fragment.

These fragments are carried by rivers and glaciers toward the sea. The Mississippi River takes more than 200 million tons (180 million tonnes) of sediment to the Gulf of Mexico each year. This accumulates as layers on the seabed, eventually to become sedimentary rocks. During its transportation, the sediment is sorted into different sizes. A strong current can carry large boulders, but a gently flowing river can carry only fine silt and mud.

The detrital rocks are classified mainly according to the size of the particles in them. Coarse-grained varieties include conglomerate and breccia (BREH-chee-uh). Conglomerate is a mass of rounded, water-worn pebbles cemented together; a breccia is made of angular pebbles. Sandstones have medium-sized grains, and fine-grained rocks include mudstone, shale, and clay.

Biogenic rocks

The biogenic sedimentary rocks are made of material that used to be living. Many limestones are composed of calcium carbonate, which has come from shellfish or other creatures. The limestones of the early Mississippian period in Europe and the United States are a mass of

---

LOOK CLOSER

Sedimentary Structures

On the surface of many sedimentary strata, there are various marks that help geologists to work out the environment in which the sediment was originally deposited. The hexagonal patterns formed by cracks in mud are an example of this type of geological clue. They form when mud dries out in the sun or wind and are common today around ponds and lakes. Mud cracks on a rock stratum indicate that the sediment was above sea level when it formed. Ripple marks, like those made by the sea on a beach, are common in sedimentary rocks. From them, geologists can work out the depth of water and the type of current that formed them. Some structures occur within the layer of sediment. Cross-bedding is where the layers are not flat but slightly curved when they are deposited. These occur in sand dunes and river deltas today. It is possible to work out the direction of wind or water current millions of years ago from these structures.

---

hardened lime mud containing fossils of creatures such as mollusks (soft-bodied invertebrates including snails and clams). The chalk of southern Britain and western Europe is made of countless small shells called coccoliths. Coal is another organic sedimentary rock. It is made from carbon that originally made up the tissues of plants. The plants were buried in thick masses under thousands of feet of sand and shale. The heat at this depth drove off the impurities in the plant remains, leaving only the carbon.

Chemical rocks

Some sedimentary rocks form chemically. They include some limestones, chert, rock salt, and gypsum (JIP-sum). Rock salt and gypsum are classed as evaporites because they form from the evaporation of salty water. This happens when inland seas or marine lagoons dry up.

CHECK THESE OUT!
✔IGNEOUS ROCK ✔LIMESTONE
✔METAMORPHIC ROCK ✔ROCK ✔SAND

Semiconductor

Material used in transistors, microchips, and other electronic devices

Conductors are materials, such as metals, through which electricity flows easily in any direction. Other materials (called insulators) are very poor electrical conductors. Between these two are semiconductors. Semiconductors can be heated to increase their conductivity and treated to allow electricity to flow in only one direction.

Electron flow

Electricity is a flow of electrons. In metals, some of the electrons are shared among all the atoms, so an electric current can flow. In nonconductors, such as wood, the electrons are shared only with neighboring atoms. The atoms are held by covalent (shared electron) bonds and the electrons cannot move away.

A metal's ability to conduct electricity decreases (its resistance increases) when the temperature rises. Its resistance also increases when there are impurities (other atoms) present. Semiconductors behave in the opposite way. The bonding electrons are held in place only weakly.

Heat (even moderate temperatures) or light can cause electrons to break free and move about.

Each electron has a negative charge, and so leaves a positively charged hole. If an electric current is applied across a semiconductor, the electrons are repelled by the negative side. The holes move away from the positive side. The electrons are called n-carriers (n for negative), and the holes p-carriers (p for positive).

Mixtures

Semiconductors can be elements or compounds. Elements that make good semiconductors include silicon (Si), germanium (Ge), and some types of tin (Sn) and lead (Pb). A pure semiconductor has an equal number of n- and p-carriers. During manufacture, other atoms are added to semiconductor crystals in order to alter this balance. This is called doping.

Uses of semiconductors

Semiconductor diodes and transistors are important components in electronic devices. Diodes pass current in one direction only. To make a diode, a semiconductor crystal is doped to make p-carriers at one end and n-carriers at the other. Where they meet, a p–n junction is formed, which can block the flow of electrons.

Semiconductor transistors amplify a current (make it larger) or switch it on and off. Transistors consist of a p–n–p or n–p–n junction. A small voltage—such as a radio signal—is applied to the base (middle) of the junction. A much stronger current is passed through the transistor and amplifies the weak signal. Transistors are used in radios and televisions.

CHECK THESE OUT!
✔ELECTRON ✔ELECTRONICS ✔METAL ✔NONMETAL

Semiconductors are used in circuit chips, where they control the flow of electricity.

Silurian Period

A period of Earth's history that lasted from 438 to 408 million years ago

The Silurian period is in the Paleozoic era, between the older Ordovician period and the younger Devonian period. The Silurian is one of the shorter sections of geologic time lasting only 30 million years from 438 to 408 million years ago. The name comes from an ancient tribe (the Silures) who lived in southern Wales nearly 2,000 years ago. The period was named in 1835 by Scottish geologist Sir Roderick Impey Murchison (1792–1871) while he was studying the rocks in Wales.

*Encrinurus, **a Silurian trilobite, lived on the ocean bed. This fossil has a perfect imprint of its tail.***

Life on Earth

The Silurian period is important in the history of the development of life on Earth. The first vascular (VAS-kyoo-luhr) plants developed at this time. These plants have veins and a fluid-transporting system. During the Silurian period, they flourished on land. This was important for the development of plant-eating reptiles and mammals in later periods. Also at this time, the first air-breathing animals (scorpions and millipedes) began to spread across the land. In the sea, many soft-bodied invertebrates (creatures with no backbone) developed. These included mollusks, brachiopods (BRAY-kee-uh-PAHDZ), and trilobites, which all lived in shallow coral reefs. In the deeper water, graptolites drifted on ocean currents, and on the seabed lived huge sea scorpions. They were arthropods (a group of animals with segmented bodies) that grew up to 9 feet (3 m) in length. They were fierce predators with sawlike teeth, and they fed on fish and invertebrates. Today, their distant descendants are the horseshoe crabs.

Silurian rocks

There are two important sedimentary rock types in the Silurian period. Over the continental shelves around the edges of the landmasses (Laurasia in the north and Gondwana in the south), there were shallow seas. On these sea beds, thick deposits of limestone, rich in fossils, were formed. There are also sandstones and shales (fine-grained sedimentary rocks) intermingled with the limestone layers. Fossils of trilobites and mollusks are common, along with corals and brachiopods. Out in the deeper water, well away from the landmasses, thick layers of shale and mud accumulated. These contain fossil graptolites. Among the layers of mudstone and shale, there are often thick masses of sandy rock. These are the deposits from currents that were fast-moving and heavy with sediment and that flowed out from the continental shelf into the deep sea. On land, there were desert conditions in North America. In the area now covered by the Great Lakes, a huge inland sea existed in a low-lying desert. This sea gradually dried out, leaving behind thick deposits of salt. These salt deposits are of considerable economic significance, supplying industrial salt to much of the United States. Other Silurian mineral deposits include iron ore in Alabama.

CHECK THESE OUT!
✔DEVONIAN PERIOD ✔FOSSIL ✔GEOLOGIC TIMESCALE
✔GONDWANA ✔ORDOVICIAN PERIOD
✔PALEOZOIC ERA

Silver

Silver was one of only a handful of metals known to ancient peoples—it has been found in royal tombs dating back to 4000 B.C.E. It is relatively rare and, of all the 90 naturally occurring elements, comes 63rd in abundance. On average, there are 0.07 grams of silver for each ton (0.9 tonnes) of Earth's crust. The element's chemical symbol, Ag, comes from the Roman name for the metal, *argentum.*

Because of its rarity, silver has always been considered a precious metal. As long ago as 2925 B.C.E., Menes, the first king of Egypt, made a law that defined its value. Two and a half parts of silver, said the law, were equivalent to one part of gold, so silver had two-fifths the value of gold.

Today, the value of silver is not so high— around one-eightieth that of gold. During the 1960s, manufacturers of camera film used so much silver that mining companies found it hard to supply enough of the metal to them. This forced the price to an all-time high, until the United States government stepped in with laws to control the buying and selling of silver.

The element can be found as pure metal, called native silver. Norway has the world's richest source of native silver. The principal ores are argentite (silver sulfide) and cerargyrite (SEH-ruhr-JY-ryt; silver chloride). Lead and copper ores also contain important amounts of silver,

which have to be recovered during the production of lead and copper metal. The chief producers of silver from ores are Canada, Mexico, Peru, Russia, and the United States.

Chemical properties

Silver belongs in group 11 (IB) of the periodic table, along with gold (Au) and copper (Cu). However, unlike copper, it normally has only one electron available to form compounds. It has the lowest melting point of these three metals, at 1760.9°F (960.5°C).

The element is gray-white and can be polished to a brilliant shine. It conducts heat and electricity better than any other metal. This makes it an ideal,

HIGHLIGHTS

◆ Silver is relatively rare. It is the 63rd most abundant element on Earth.

◆ Silver is the best conductor of heat and electricity of all metals.

◆ Although it does not easily oxidize in air, silver is affected by sulfur compounds in the air and forms a black coating of tarnish.

◆ Silver compounds are used in photography.

although expensive, material for electric wiring and contact points (junctions between conductors) in electronic circuits. The metal is easily worked (molded into different shapes) and can be pulled into wires.

Silver is not very reactive and does not oxidize easily in air. This was one of the reasons that it was first used to make coins and jewelry.

However, ever since fossil fuels (coal, oil, and gas) began to be burned for energy, air has often contained sulfur compounds. These react with silver to produce black silver sulfide, which is the principal cause of silver tarnishing (dulling and coloring). An alloy (mixture) of 92.5 percent silver and 7.5 percent copper is called sterling silver. It resists tarnishing and is used for jewelry and cutlery. It is also more resistant to scratching than pure silver.

Alloys of silver with gold form the "yellow gold" used in jewelry and are also used by dentists to cap and fill teeth. Most silver compounds are insoluble in water. The main exception to this is silver nitrate. When sodium or potassium cyanide is added to a solution of silver nitrate, a compound is formed that contains the silver cyanide ion, $Ag(CN)_2^{-1}$. This is used in electroplating (coating another metal with a layer

Silver can be found as a pure metal, called native silver. Here, it has formed as a twisted loop of wires.

> ## LOOK CLOSER
>
> # Silver Compounds
>
> Probably the most important use of silver is in photography. The three halides (compounds formed with halogen elements)—silver chloride, silver bromide, and silver iodide—are all sensitive to light and have all been employed in photography. When a plate or film coated with these chemicals is exposed to light, the silver halide begins to decompose, releasing metallic silver. After a normal exposure in a camera, there is no visible image. However, the tiny spots of silver can be developed into larger areas in the darkroom, producing the familiar "negative" image.
>
> A different use has been developed for silver iodide. Tiny crystals of this compound can be used to "seed" clouds and cause rain. The crystals are dropped from an aircraft and cause droplets of water to gather around them, until the drops are large enough to fall as rain.
>
> Silver compounds are also used in medicine. Silver nitrate will blacken and kill skin cells. It has been used to treat warts. Silver oxide kills bacteria and can be used to purify water.
>
> Silver azide is a compound of one atom of silver with three atoms of nitrogen. It is very unstable and has been used as a detonator for explosives.
>
> The starting point for the preparation of most silver compounds is silver nitrate, the only simple silver salt that is easily soluble in water. It is made by dissolving metallic silver in nitric acid.

of silver). The object to be plated is placed in a silver cyanide solution, with a block of pure silver. An electric current is passed from the silver to the other object through the solution. Silver atoms are deposited on the object, while others dissolve from the silver block into the cyanide solution. Another silver solution can be formed with ammonia (NH_3). This is used to make silver-backed mirrors.

CHECK THESE OUT!
✔COPPER ✔ELECTROLYSIS ✔ELECTRONICS ✔GOLD
✔METAL ✔OXIDATION ✔PHOTOGRAPHY ✔SMELTING

Smelting

Nearly all the metal in the world occurs naturally in the form of ores. The metal is generally combined with oxygen or sulfur and must be freed using chemical reactions. The most common method of doing this is smelting. The ore is mixed with other materials and heated to a very high temperature in a furnace.

When the ore is dug from the ground, it is mixed up with rock and other waste. This waste matter is called gangue (GAHNG). As much gangue as possible must be removed before smelting. Treatments called ore dressing are used to concentrate the metallic mineral from the gangue. First, the ore and rock are crushed mechanically. These materials are often of different densities, and the gangue can be washed away with water or another suitable liquid. If this does not work, flotation can be used. In flotation, the crushed material is mixed with water and an oil that attracts the mineral but not the gangue. Air is blown into the mixture to produce a floating froth of oily mineral, which can be skimmed off and dried. Some iron ores are magnetic and can be separated from the gangue using an electromagnet.

HIGHLIGHTS

◆ Ores are first crushed and concentrated to remove the waste rock, or gangue.

◆ Smelting in a high-temperature furnace produces molten metal, slag, and waste gases.

◆ Smelting sulfide ores is responsible for the development of acid rain, a serious pollutant.

◆ Copper was first smelted around 4000 B.C.E., and iron around 2500 B.C.E.

Smelting iron ore

Iron ore is usually an oxide, hematite, or magnetite. It is smelted in a blast furnace, a tapered tower 100 to 120 feet (30 to 36 m) high. The furnace is kept running continuously, with new charge—a mixture of ore, coke, and limestone—being added at intervals at the top of the tower as the molten iron and waste material (slag) are drawn off. About 35 feet (10.5 m) from the bottom of the tower is a ring of holes called tuyeres (twee-ERS). Hot air with added oxygen is blasted through these holes. The hottest region is just above the tuyeres. Here, the carbon in the coke reacts with oxygen, producing carbon dioxide and raising the temperature to 3600°F (2000°C). The hot carbon dioxide rises through the descending charge. It reacts with

After smelting, iron is refined further to produce molten steel.

more carbon to produce carbon monoxide. This reaction uses heat: in the middle of the furnace the temperature is only around 1800°F (1000°C).

The carbon monoxide then reacts with the iron oxide, producing molten iron and carbon dioxide. The iron sinks to the bottom of the furnace; the carbon dioxide and other waste gases are released near the top. The limestone in the charge reacts with the gangue to produce molten slag that floats on top of the iron and protects it from becoming oxidized again. The molten iron is tapped off into branches of sand molds. This arrangement looks like a sow with feeding piglets, and so the iron produced is called pig iron.

Smelting copper ore

Copper ore is smelted in a reverberatory (ri-VEHR-buh-ruh-TOHR-ee) furnace, which is smaller than a blast furnace and a different shape. A typical furnace is about 25 feet (7.5 m) wide. It has an arched roof, with walls that are about 10 feet (3 m) high on each side.

Most copper ores, such as chalcopyrite and bornite, are sulfides that contain large quantities of iron. After crushing and flotation, the ore goes first to a furnace where it is roasted in air to remove some of the sulfur. Then it is smelted in the reverberatory furnace. Burning fuel and hot air enter the side of the furnace and flow (reverberate) around the walls, until the charge melts at 2552°F (1400°C).

The copper sulfide reacts with oxygen to produce sulfur dioxide and molten copper, which collects on the bottom of the furnace. The iron sulfide reacts with the walls of the furnace, releasing more sulfur dioxide and forming a molten slag, which floats on top of the copper. The impure copper, called matte, is tapped off and refined in a furnace called a converter. The product—blister copper—is 99 percent pure.

Smelting lead and silver ore

The most important ore of lead is galena, or lead sulfide. The ore is crushed and then roasted to remove sulfur and make the fine particles clump together. This process is called sintering. The ore is then smelted with coke and limestone in a blast furnace similar to that used for iron ore. The impure lead produced is called base bullion.

A copper mine and smeltery. The barren landscape shows the harmful effects of sulfur dioxide in the air.

As much as two-thirds of Earth's silver is found in copper, lead, and zinc ores. Lead-silver sulfide ores are smelted in the same way as galena. To extract the silver from the molten base bullion, zinc is added. The zinc forms an alloy (mixture) with the silver, which floats on the lead. This alloy is tapped off and then heated to remove the zinc. Copper-silver ores are smelted in the same way as copper ore. The blister contains the silver, which is then recovered by electrolysis when the copper is refined.

Acid rain

Smelting sulfide ores releases sulfur dioxide into the atmosphere, where it reacts with oxygen and water vapor to produce sulfuric acid. This acid has caused serious acid rain pollution for more than 150 years. Smelteries are sited away from towns because of concerns about air quality. However, the effect of acid rain on crops and forests is still a problem. International efforts are being made to reduce smelter gas emission.

CHECK THESE OUT!
✔COPPER ✔IRON AND STEEL ✔METAL ✔METALLURGY ✔MINING ✔ORE ✔OXIDATION ✔POLLUTION ✔SILVER

Solar System

The Sun and all the objects that move around it, including the planets

Everything that orbits the Earth's Sun under the influence of its gravity is part of the Solar System. The Sun is one star among billions in the Milky Way, and astronomers now know of many other stars with planets in orbit around them. However, Earth's Solar System is the only one known to contain a planet that supports life.

The Solar System contains billions of separate objects. The best known are the nine planets: Mercury, Venus, Earth, Mars, Jupiter, Saturn, Uranus, Neptune, and Pluto. Many of these have moons in orbit around them, and there are also countless objects—comets, asteroids, and dust particles—in independent orbits around the Sun.

The Sun

The heart of the Solar System is Earth's star, the Sun. This huge ball of gas, 865,000 miles (1.4 million km) across, is the source of all the heat and light that has enabled life to evolve on Earth. The Sun is even responsible for driving the geological activity on all the planets. The Sun formed around 4.6 billion years ago, and the planets formed from the material left behind.

The Sun's energy comes from atomic fusion in its core. This releases intense radiation, which takes thousands of years to force its way to the surface and then blazes out across the Solar System as visible light, heat, and other types of radiation. The intensity of energy from the Sun drops rapidly as it travels across the Solar

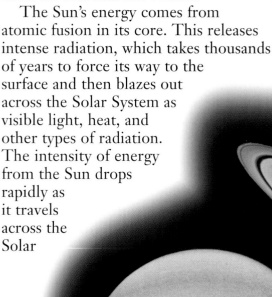

HIGHLIGHTS

- ◆ The Solar System consists of a star (the Sun) surrounded by nine planets, dozens of moons, billions of asteroids and comets, interplanetary dust, and the solar wind.

- ◆ Mercury, Venus, Earth, and Mars are the four inner, terrestrial planets—relatively small and made mostly of metals and minerals.

- ◆ Jupiter, Saturn, Uranus, and Neptune are the outer gas giant planets. Each of the giant planets has a huge family of moons.

- ◆ Pluto, the ninth planet, is thought to be the largest of a belt of cometlike objects.

- ◆ The Solar System formed 4.6 billion years ago.

System—the surface of Mercury, the closest planet to the Sun, is heated to around 800°F (450°C), while that of Pluto, the most distant planet, never rises above −330°F (−200°C).

Although the Sun's heat and light diminish rapidly across the Solar System, the Sun still has an important influence through the solar wind—a stream of charged particles blasted out from the Sun's surface. The solar wind blows across the Solar System at speeds of up to 440 miles per second (700 km/s), until it reaches a boundary called the heliopause (HEE-lee-uh-PAWZ), where it runs into the force of stellar winds from thousands of other nearby stars and forms a shock wave (violent disturbance in the wave pattern). Some astronomers regard the heliopause as the true boundary of the Solar System, although they are not sure how far beyond the orbit of Pluto it lies.

Terrestrial planets

The region closest to the Sun is home to the terrestrial (Earthlike) planets—Mercury, Venus, Earth itself, and Mars. These planets orbit in a relatively tiny, inner region of the Solar System. The terrestrial planets are made mostly of rocks and metals. Mercury is the smallest and densest world, while Venus,

A photo collage showing the planets in the Solar System (except Pluto) from Neptune, looking back toward Earth, the Moon, and the inner planets.

Earth, and Mars all have similar compositions. There is also the Earth's Moon, with the lowest density of any object in this inner Solar System.

All the terrestrial planets have atmospheres, though Mercury's is very thin and is made up of just a few scattered atoms of metal vapor. The planets probably started out with similar atmospheres, made of hydrogen compounds. However, they have evolved in very different ways since these early times.

Mercury

Tiny Mercury would be a brilliant object in the sky, but it orbits so close to the Sun that it is lost in the glare and is only visible from Earth at dawn and dusk. Mercury's weak gravity caused it to lose most of its atmosphere early in its history. Its interior cooled down rapidly because of the planet's small size. The planet shows no sign of recent geological activity. As a result, Mercury is covered in ancient craters caused by the impact of meteorites, and it looks like the Moon.

Venus

Venus is slightly smaller than Earth and has a thick atmosphere, so astronomers once thought it was likely to be able to support life. This was an illusion, however, as it is the most hostile place in the Solar System. Venus may once have had oceans, but they evaporated as the Sun heated up. This left a dry planet with a choking atmosphere of carbon dioxide and surface temperatures hot enough to melt lead. The lack of water also stopped the formation of continental plates like Earth's, so heat could only escape through volcanoes.

Earth

The Earth formed in a narrow temperature zone around the Sun where liquid water is stable. This had a crucial effect on the way the planet works, allowing the formation of continental plates, which drift around the planet. Water was also vital to the evolution of life. In turn, early forms of life converted the early volcanic atmosphere into the hospitable air we breathe today. Earth's Moon is an airless world, and it probably formed when the Earth collided with a Mars-sized planet early in its history.

Mars

Mars is a smaller planet than Earth or Venus, with a thin atmosphere, but is the most Earthlike of the other planets. The interior of Mars cooled too fast for continental plates to form, but the planet has extinct volcanoes and chasms (KA-zuhmz; deep clefts in the surface), polar ice caps, and signs of flowing water and floods in its distant past. There is also evidence of flowing water on the planet's surface in the recent past. Astronomers disagree about whether this shows that the planet could have supported life.

Asteroids

Between Mars and Jupiter (the first planet in the outer Solar System) lies a swarm of smaller rocky objects, the asteroid belt. These tiny worlds range from Ceres, more than 550 miles (900 km) across, to billions of tiny chunks of rock a few yards across. There are estimated to be over 10 billion asteroids more than 330 feet (100 m) across. Together, they might have formed into a small planet if they had not been disrupted by the pull of Jupiter's gravity.

Asteroids are not confined to this belt. The inner Solar System is swarming with objects in elliptical (squashed circular) orbits, many of which pass close to, or cross, Earth's orbit. There are an estimated 330,000 of these near-Earth asteroids more than 330 feet (100 m) across, and many smaller objects (meteoroids) that sometimes plunge into Earth's atmosphere, burning up as meteors or landing as meteorites.

Another group of asteroids are the Trojans, which share their orbit with Jupiter but travel ahead of and behind the giant planet. There are even some mysterious objects, such as Chiron, moving in highly elliptical orbits between the outer planets. These may be burned-out comets.

Giant planets

Beyond the main asteroid belt lie the gas giant planets: Jupiter, Saturn, Uranus, and Neptune. These worlds are huge by comparison with the terrestrial planets—Jupiter is 11 times Earth's diameter—and have very different compositions. Although they have rocky cores, they formed mainly from gases and ices that could not exist in the inner Solar System. Jupiter and Saturn form

LOOK CLOSER

Formation of the Sun

The Sun is thought to have formed around 4.6 billion years ago when a shock wave from an exploding star passed through a huge interstellar cloud of gas and dust and triggered its collapse. Over millions of years before, this cloud had become stretched and flattened by the rotation of the galaxy. After the collision, it began to clump together under its own gravity and rotate (picture A, below), forming a rotating disk with a bulge at its center—the young Sun (picture B, below). The more mass the Sun collected, the stronger its gravity became, and the faster it rotated.

As more gas poured into the Sun, the pressure and temperature in its core began to increase. At first the Sun released energy as infrared (heat) radiation (picture C, below), but eventually conditions in the core reached a point where nuclear fusion of hydrogen into helium could begin, releasing the energy that still powers the Sun today.

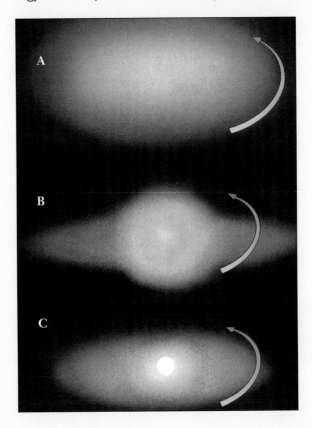

How the Sun formed from a dust and gas cloud.

a pair of gas giants dominated by hydrogen and helium, while Uranus and Neptune are sometimes called "ice giants" because they are made mostly of ices that condensed from gases in the cold outer reaches of the Solar System.

All the giant planets have ring systems, although Saturn's is the most magnificent. The rings are made up of billions of particles, each in its own orbit around the parent planet. The size of these particles varies widely—Saturn's brilliant rings are made up of boulder- and house-sized chunks of ice, while Jupiter's faint rings are made of dust-sized particles. Astronomers think that rings form when a comet breaks up or collides

with a moon close to the parent planet. Over thousands of years, collisions grind down the size of the ring particles, and the planet's gravity pulls material down into its atmosphere, so rings may have relatively short lives.

Jupiter

Jupiter is large enough to swallow all the other planets in the Solar System. The planet's surface is dominated by huge, brightly colored weather systems, including the Great Red Spot, a storm larger than the Earth. While the outer planets receive less heat from the Sun, all except Uranus generate heat inside themselves. This helps to power their violent weather. Jupiter's enormous gravity allows the planet to grab or deflect comets and other objects approaching from the outer Solar System, protecting the terrestrial planets from harm.

Saturn

Saturn is not as colorful as Jupiter, but it has weather systems that are even more violent. They are hidden, however, underneath an outer layer of white haze. The planet is the least dense in the Solar System—it would float in water and has difficulty holding itself together as it spins, resulting in a bulge at the equator (imaginary line that circles a planet halfway between the poles).

Uranus

Uranus is tipped sideways, tilted in its orbit so that, surrounded by its rings, it looks like an archery target. The tilt was probably caused by

LOOK CLOSER

Orbits

The planets move around the Sun in ellipses, most of which are relatively close to being perfect circles. These orbits all fall roughly in the same plane, which extends from the Sun through Earth's orbit (called the ecliptic). Pluto, however, is an exception—it has a highly elliptical orbit (see diagram below) and is tilted at 17 degrees to the ecliptic.

Distances in the Solar System are measured in astronomical units (AU). One AU is the average distance from Earth to the Sun (93 million miles or 150 million km). The planets and their average distances from the Sun are: Mercury (0.39 AU), Venus (0.72 AU), Earth (1.00 AU), Mars (1.52 AU), Jupiter (5.20 AU), Saturn (9.58 AU), Uranus (19.12 AU), Neptune (30.11 AU), and Pluto (39.31 AU).

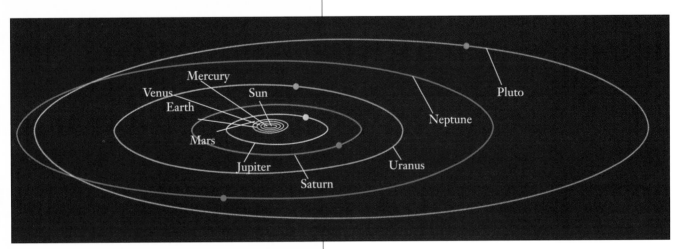

a collision with another object early in the planet's history. Unlike the other gas giants, Uranus has no violent weather patterns and does not generate energy from its interior.

Neptune

Neptune is similar in size to Uranus (around five times the diameter of Earth) and also in composition. It has violent storms, including the Great Dark Spot, which rivals the largest storms on Jupiter. Neptune's rings are strange. They include several "ring arcs"—swarms of material that are not spread evenly around the ring orbit.

Outer moons

All the giants have large families of moons made from the material left behind after the planets formed. The composition of the moons varies—Jupiter's are rocky, but from Saturn outward, the moons are mostly icy. Some of the outer moons are large enough to be worlds in themselves. Jupiter has 16 satellites , including four giant moons: Io, Europa, Ganymede, and Callisto.

Artwork showing the planets, the asteroid belt, and a comet whose orbit crosses that of Earth.

These moons are pulled by Jupiter's and each other's gravity, which makes them heat up. Io is the most volcanically active world in the Solar System. Ice-covered Europa may have a liquid water ocean underground, undersea volcanoes, and perhaps even life beneath its surface. Ganymede shows signs of tectonic plates, and Callisto may also have an underground ocean.

Saturn's family of at least 18 satellites includes giant Titan. This is the only moon with a thick atmosphere, which may be like those that formed on the young terrestrial planets. Astronomers think its surface is covered in slicks of oily tar.

Uranus has more than 20 moons, including Miranda, which seems to have been broken apart and reassembled in its recent past and shows almost every type of surface seen elsewhere in the Solar System. Neptune's system, meanwhile, is dominated by frozen Triton, which has erupting ice geysers (GEE-zuhrz; jets) on its

LOOK CLOSER

Formation of the Planets

As the Sun began to shine, a huge disk of material was left in orbit around it. The Sun's gravity had pulled in most of the gas from the inner cloud, and what was left behind close to the Sun was soon blasted out of the Solar System by the solar wind. Most of the material in the inner Solar System was created from dust. Over millions of years, the dust particles began to collide and stick together, until some had enough gravity to pull other material in. These "planetesimals" grew to form planets. Each collision released heat, melting and re-forming the growing planets into spheres with heavy cores and lighter material toward the crust. This heating released gases, which were trapped by gravity to form early atmospheres.

The outer Solar System was colder and the solar wind less fierce, so gas and ice survived. The solid cores may have formed first, building up in the same way as the terrestrial planets, and sweeping up atmospheres of gas and ice. Another theory is that turbulence broke the gas cloud into chunks, each condensing into a planet under its own gravity, with the heavier dust particles falling to the cores of the planets. On the outer edge of the Solar System, Triton, Pluto, and the Kuiper belt objects were created from ice. They never got hot enough to melt completely, or they would have evaporated.

In this picture of the Sun, visible light has been blocked to show the ultraviolet part of the spectrum.

surface and is probably a captured world from the depths of the Solar System.

Pluto and beyond

The outermost known planet, Pluto, is now thought to be just the largest and closest member of a group of icy outer worlds, mostly asteroid-sized, called the Kuiper (KOY-puhr) belt. This belt was probably also the origin of Neptune's moon, Triton. Pluto orbits the Sun in a highly elongated path, and it has a satellite called Charon, which is so large that the two worlds are considered a double-planet system.

Several much smaller members of the Kuiper belt have been found in recent years, but these tiny bodies are very different from the inner asteroids, as they are made mostly of ice. The Kuiper belt may be a source of comets, which fall into the inner Solar System and grow tails of gas and dust as they heat up near the Sun. Astronomers have suggested that there might be another large planet, Planet X, orbiting within or beyond the Kuiper belt. If Planet X does exist, it must be distant, dark, and cold. As it passes through the Kuiper belt, it could be responsible for sending comets plunging on their long journey into the inner Solar System.

Far beyond the Kuiper belt, astronomers believe the Solar System is surrounded by a ball-shaped shell of icy bodies called the Oort (OHRT) cloud, stretching out to one light-year from the Sun. The Oort cloud and Kuiper belt could be the remains of the icy building blocks of the Solar System, left in the cold outer darkness while material closer to the Sun formed the planets.

CHECK THESE OUT!

✔ASTEROID ✔ASTRONOMY ✔COMET
✔COSMOLOGY ✔JUPITER ✔MARS ✔MERCURY
✔METEOR ✔MOON ✔NEPTUNE ✔PLUTO ✔SATURN
✔STAR ✔SUN ✔UNIVERSE ✔URANUS ✔VENUS

Solid

Matter can exist in three different states (forms) called solid, liquid, and gas. All matter consists of particles that may be atoms, molecules, or ions. In a solid, the particles are packed closely together. They do not move very much, only vibrate about fixed points—like people jostling each other in a crowd. Because their particles are packed so tightly, solids have a fixed shape and are difficult to compress (squeeze together).

The three states

Gas particles move rapidly in all directions. A gas expands to fill any space and can be compressed (squeezed) into a smaller space. The particles in a liquid move with less energy than in a gas and cling loosely to each other, so liquids are difficult to compress. Liquids do not have a fixed shape because the particles can slip past one another.

HIGHLIGHTS

◆ Unlike gases, which spread in all directions, and liquids, which flow to fit the shape of a container, solids have a fixed shape and volume.

◆ The particles in a solid are packed closely together. Solids are difficult to compress.

◆ All true solids are crystalline.

◆ The atoms or molecules in a crystal are arranged in a regular network called a lattice.

The crystalline (regular) structure of a solid (sodium chloride) can be seen through a microscope.

Solids are usually hard and difficult to stretch or cut because their particles are held in position by their neighbors. However, the bonds between the particles are not completely rigid (RIH-jid; stiff). Applying an external force makes the atoms move slightly closer together. When the force is removed, the atoms move back to their original positions. When a solid is stretched—up to a certain limit—the forces between the atoms will restore the solid to its original shape when the external force is removed. This property of solids is called elasticity. When a solid is heated, the vibrations of its atoms increase and so the bonds between the atoms become slightly longer. The solid therefore expands slightly with an increase in temperature. This is called thermal expansion.

Crystals

When a person views sugar granules through a microscope, he or she sees tiny glassy cubes. These cubes are sugar crystals. Gemstones such as rubies and sapphires are also crystals. All true solids, including metals, are made of crystals.

The atoms or molecules in a crystal form a three-dimensional structure called a lattice (LA-tuhs) in which the particles are arranged in a regular network. The atoms in a lattice line up as neatly as the sections of a chain-link fence. The shape of the lattice gives the crystal its particular shape and color. Many substances in solution form crystals when the solution is cooled. When solids are heated to form molten liquids, most form crystals as they cool.

When heated, ice melts and becomes water. When ice, or any other solid, is heated, its particles gain energy and vibrate more. The regular arrangement of the particles breaks down and, at the solid's melting point, the particles vibrate so much that they break away from their positions. The solid becomes a liquid. Like ice, even iron and diamond can melt to become a liquid and boil to become a gas.

Every pure substance has a characteristic melting point, which changes if even a tiny amount of another substance is mixed with it. In this way, the melting point of a substance can be used to identify it and to tell whether it is pure.

Conductors, insulators, and magnets

The crystals of all the metals and those of a few nonmetals, such as graphite (GRA-FYT; a form of carbon) can conduct electricity because their atoms easily lose electrons. These electrons can then move freely through the crystal and produce an electric current when a voltage is applied. In an insulator (nonconductor), such as rubber, glass, or plastic, the electrons are too tightly bound to the molecules to be able to move in an external electric field. The magnetic properties of a solid, in contrast, depend on the bound electrons. Normally the electrons form pairs, canceling out each other's magnetism. A few elements, for example, iron, cobalt, and nickel, have unpaired electrons that line up with the magnetic fields of the electrons in neighboring atoms to produce a powerful overall magnetism.

CHECK THESE OUT!
✔ATOM ✔CRYSTAL ✔ELASTICITY ✔ELECTRON ✔GAS ✔LIQUID ✔MATTER ✔METAL ✔MOLECULE

LOOK CLOSER

Sublimation

Sublimation (SUH-bluh-MAY-shun) is the name given to the process by which a solid changes directly into a gas without first becoming a liquid. Just as when a liquid is heated and evaporates (turns to a gas), sublimation occurs when particles of a solid gain enough energy to jump free of the surface. One of the best places to see sublimation is at the theater when dry ice (solid carbon dioxide frozen at very low temperatures) is used. The cold carbon dioxide gas causes atmospheric moisture to condense, producing clouds of misty vapor. Iodine sublimes in a similar way. At room temperature, iodine consists of black crystals. If the crystals are heated, they form a purple vapor. When cooled, the vapor turns back to iodine crystals without going through a liquid stage.

Dry ice (solid carbon dioxide) sublimates to form a cloudy, white gas at room temperature.

Sound

Waves of energy generated by objects vibrating in the environment

People rely on sound in many situations. Sound makes it possible to speak and hear. It also has a range of unexpected uses. A type of scanning, using ultrasound, makes it possible to see babies in the womb. A method of studying the way sound travels through Earth, called seismography (syz-MAH-gruh-fee), helps scientists understand earthquakes and locate valuable underground minerals, such as oil.

What is sound?

Sound is created when things vibrate (move back and forth). When a guitar player plucks a guitar string, the string moves rapidly up and down. Each time the string moves up, it squeezes the air very slightly and each time it moves down, it stretches the air. This stretching and squeezing of the air sets up invisible waves between the guitar string and a listener's ears. Inside the ear, a small membrane called the eardrum—very much like the skin of a musical drum—vibrates when the sound waves reach it. Cells in this membrane convert the vibration into a signal, which is carried to the brain by the auditory nerve.

Sound is a vibration in the air or another medium (the general name for anything that sound travels through), which is detected by the ears and brain. The medium is very important— without something to carry the vibrations, there can be no sound. Although sound can travel quite easily through water and even through the rocks inside Earth, it cannot

Ear protectors are padded to absorb sound waves. This prevents loud sounds from damaging the ears.

HIGHLIGHTS

♦ Sound travels four times faster in water than in air and even faster through solids.

♦ All sounds can be described in terms of three properties: frequency, intensity, and timbre.

♦ Sound has many uses, from studying earthquakes to imaging unborn babies in the womb.

travel through a vacuum (VA-kyoom; a completely empty space).

Anything that vibrates makes a sound. String instruments make their sounds with strings that vibrate when they are plucked. Woodwind instruments make sounds when air vibrates inside their hollow tubes. Voices make sounds when air vibrates in the vocal cords inside the throat.

Describing sounds

In theory, vibrating objects can make an infinite number of different sounds. Nevertheless, many everyday sounds do have a lot in common with one another. A piano and a guitar can play the same note, for example, or they may play different notes at the same volume (loudness). Scientists have found that they can tell one sound from another by describing it with three different terms: intensity (related to volume), frequency (pitch), and timbre (TAM-buhr; quality).

The intensity of a sound depends on how much the object vibrates. The bigger the vibration, the greater the intensity. When a drum is hit very hard, the drum skin goes up and down by a much bigger amount than when it is tapped softly. Banging the drum produces a sound of much greater intensity, which is heard as a much louder sound. Intensity and loudness are not exactly the same thing, but more intense vibrations do sound louder to the ear.

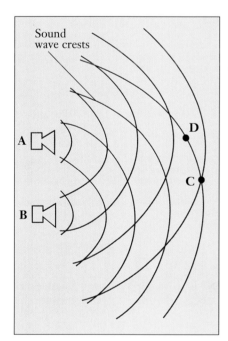

Sound travels in waves. The waves from two loudspeakers (A and B) interfere with one another. At point C, where wave crest meets wave crest, this produces a bigger wave and a louder sound. At point D, where crest meets trough, the waves cancel each other out and produce no sound.

EVERYDAY SCIENCE

Microphones and Loudspeakers

It is easy to send sound waves over short distances by speaking or shouting. However, sound is harder to transmit over longer distances, such as from one country to another. Because sound travels as a vibration in the air, it can be interfered with by the weather. A better way of sending sound over long distances is to convert it into an electrical signal, which can be carried over wires or as a radio wave and then converted back into sound by the receiver. Microphones and loudspeakers are the pieces of equipment that do this job.

A microphone converts sound energy into an electrical signal. One type of microphone has a thin vibrating skin, called a diaphragm (DY-uh-fram), which is like the skin of a drum. As sound waves hit the diaphragm, it vibrates and moves a packet of tiny carbon granules. This generates the electrical signal.

A loudspeaker works in the opposite way. The electrical signal from a microphone or another piece of audio (AW-dee-oh; sound-producing) equipment is fed into an electromagnet (a magnet that can be switched on or off by electricity). This creates a changing magnetic field that pulls a large diaphragm back and forth, recreating the original sound waves.

The frequency is the number of times that the object making the sound vibrates each second. Frequency is measured in units called Hertz (Hz): 1 Hz represents one vibration per second. The more often the object vibrates, the higher the frequency. For example, if a guitar string moves up and down 261 times per second, it is vibrating with a frequency of 261 Hz, which is the musical note middle C.

The timbre of a sound is what distinguishes one instrument from another. A guitar and a piano may play the same musical note (the same frequency of sound) at the same intensity, but the two instruments still sound very different. The musical notes produced by an instrument do not consist of single, pure sounds. Instead, each note consists of a basic frequency called the fundamental and a number of higher frequencies called harmonics. Together, these sound a bit like

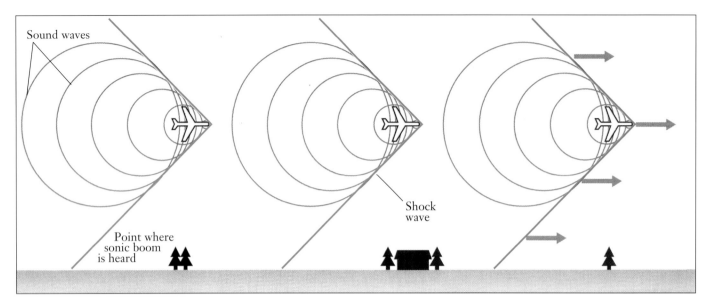

As a supersonic plane flies overhead, an area of concentrated sound called a shock wave moves along with the plane. This intense sound is called a sonic boom and is heard where the shock wave meets the ground.

a barbershop quartet. Different instruments produce different patterns of harmonics, and it is this that gives each instrument's sound its timbre.

Speed of sound

Sound travels at different speeds through different media. It travels more quickly in solids and liquids than in gases. The speed of sound in water is around four times faster than it is in air. Sound travels over 15 times faster through solid steel than through air. Sound nevertheless travels almost a million times more slowly than light.

LOOK CLOSER — Resonance

If someone wets his or her finger and runs it around the rim of a wine glass, the glass starts to sing with a musical note of a particular frequency. Different glasses produce different musical notes. Any object will tend to vibrate at a certain frequency. A cello will vibrate at a much lower frequency than a violin, for example. The way in which things vibrate at certain frequencies is called resonance. Although resonance is useful in musical instruments, it can sometimes be a nuisance. Bridges have sometimes collapsed when the wind has made them vibrate up and down at their resonant frequency.

This explains why thunder and lightning do not seem to happen at the same time. When lightning strikes, the flash of light travels at a speed of 186,282 miles per second (299,792 km/s) to the human eye. The thunder clap travels at the much slower speed of sound—around 1,086 feet per second (331 m/s).

When a jet airplane passes overhead, the sound it makes seems to lag behind. This is because it takes time for the sound from the jet engines to reach people on the ground. If the plane is flying at supersonic speeds (faster than the speed of sound; only Concorde and a few military planes do this), people on the ground hear a "sonic boom" caused by a shock wave set up by the plane. The occupants do not hear it because they are traveling faster than the sound.

Sound waves

Sound travels through air with a wave motion similar to the movement of water waves on the sea. Just as sea waves reflect off the shore, so sound waves can bounce off nearby walls or other obstacles. An echo is simply a sound wave that has reached an object, such as a wall, and bounced back to a person's ears some time after the original sound was created.

Sound waves are not entirely reflected when they meet obstacles. Unless the obstacle is very large, a portion of the wave moves around an obstacle in its path, bending around corners or passing through openings. This property of sound is called diffraction, and it explains why sounds can be heard around corners or through partly open doorways. Just as water waves can combine with other water waves to produce stronger or weaker waves, so sound waves can add together or subtract from one another. This is called interference. When setting up loudspeakers for a hi-fi system, it is very important to position them so that the sound waves from one speaker do not cancel out those from the other speaker.

Like other types of waves, sound waves bend when they move across a boundary from one type of material to another. This is called refraction. The same wave behavior makes a straw look bent when it stands half in and half out of water because of the refraction of light waves traveling through air and water. It is refraction that controls how sounds produced by earthquakes move through different types of rocks inside Earth. Scientists can find out a great deal about

*Preparing to launch **GLORIA**—a sonar device with a scanning range of about 27 miles (40 km).*

Earth's structure by studying refracted waves. This science is called seismology, and it can be used to locate minerals buried inside the planet.

Uses of sound

Scientists use sonar (*so*und *na*vigation *r*anging) equipment to detect objects underwater. Sonar devices work by sending out sound waves that are then reflected back. Sound of very high frequencies, called ultrasound, can be used by doctors to produce images of unborn babies in the womb. Similar techniques are used to test mechanical parts for defects. Ultrasound beams of much higher intensity can be used to clean difficult-to-reach parts inside complex machinery.

Acoustics is the practical science of sound. It is applied by architects designing concert halls and is used to reduce unwanted noise from construction sites. One application of acoustics is in forensic science (using scientific techniques to solve crimes). Forensic scientists can study the unique pattern of a suspect's voice to match it with a telephone call or voice tape. Acoustics has also been important in developing computer software that recognizes human speech.

CHECK THESE OUT!
✔ACOUSTICS ✔AERODYNAMICS ✔DOPPLER EFFECT
✔ULTRASOUND ✔WAVES

South America

The fourth largest continent on Earth

South America is the world's fourth largest continent, after Asia, Africa, and North America. It covers 6.88 million square miles (17.8 million sq km), about 13 percent of Earth's dry land. Roughly triangular in shape, the continent lies east as well as south of North America. In the west, the coast of Peru lies due south of the Atlantic coast of Florida. The two continents are connected by the Isthmus (IS-muhs) of Panama. This bridge of land narrows to 50 miles (80 km) at one point.

South America is nearly as long as North America but, on average, only two-thirds as wide. Its greatest east–west distance is around 3,200 miles (5,150 km). The continent stretches 4,750 miles (7,650 km) from Panama in the north to Cape Horn in the far south. Northern and eastern coasts are bounded by the Atlantic Ocean. The Pacific Ocean borders the west coast. The line of the equator runs through the mouth of the Amazon River in the northeast.

Natural features

The Amazon in South America is Earth's largest river. This mighty river flows 4,000 miles (6,440 km) across the north and center of the

Map showing mainland South America, the Andes Mountains, and the Amazon and its tributaries.

continent and carries one-fifth of the world's fresh flowing water. The Amazon Basin (area of land from which water flows into the Amazon) is the world's largest river basin. It is bordered by the Guiana (gee-AH-nuh) Highlands to the north, the Brazilian Highlands to the south, and the Andes Mountains to the west.

The Andes run for 5,500 miles (8,850 km) along the west coast of the continent. They are the world's second highest mountain range, after the Himalayas in Asia. The Andes chain includes many summits above 20,000 feet (6,100 m), including many volcanoes. Earthquakes are also common in South America. Most of the

---

HIGHLIGHTS

♦ Earth's biggest river, the Amazon, flows across northern and central South America.

♦ South America's Andes Mountains are the second highest mountain range in the world after the Himalayas. They were formed by movements of the tectonic plates that make up Earth's crust.

♦ Much of South America has a tropical climate. The seasons are exactly opposite from those experienced in North America.

LOOK CLOSER

Climate of South America

Lying in the Southern Hemisphere, South America experiences its seasons at opposite times of the year from North America. South America covers a wide range of latitudes (covers a great north–south distance) and experiences a variety of climates. A large part of the continent lies in the equatorial zone (30 degrees north and south of the equator). Tropical conditions prevail in most of this area.

The northerly part of South America and the Amazon region experience high daytime temperatures, between 82° and 100°F (28° to 38°C). At night, temperatures seldom drop below 65°F (18°C). Rainfall is heavy all year (3 to 12 inches or 8 to 31 cm per month). Humidity (moisture content of the air) is always high.

South of the equatorial zone, temperatures vary with the seasons, but within a narrow range compared to North America. Southern Brazil, Uruguay, and the pampas of eastern Argentina have a climate similar to the southeastern United States. Farther south, the climate of Patagonia is more similar to the dry plains and deserts of southern and western Texas. The southern tip of the continent, close to Antarctica, has a cold, damp climate.

Three main factors influence South America's climate. First, cold ocean currents flowing along the Pacific coast affect the pattern of rainfall and air temperatures in the west. Second, the Andes Mountain range creates a large rain shadow (an area where rain is rare) in the southern part of the continent.

Third and most important is the presence of high-pressure air masses over the South Atlantic and South Pacific. These affect wind patterns and rainfall over tropical and subtropical South America. The two air masses shift their positions according to the season. Between them lies a wet zone called the intertropical convergence zone (ITCZ). For much of the year, the ITCZ rests over the Amazon basin, bringing long periods of heavy rain to these lowlands, which form South America's Amazonian rain forests (see picture). In midwinter (June in South America), the moisture-laden zone moves northward, bringing somewhat drier weather to the Amazon region.

continent's large cities have been damaged by earthquakes at some time.

The Andes region holds many lakes, including the continent's largest body of fresh water, Lake Titicaca, which lies across the border of Peru and Bolivia. At 12,500 feet (3,810 m) above sea level, this is the highest lake of this size on Earth.

The plains of Argentina, east of the Andes, are called the pampas. They cover 300,000 square miles (777,000 sq km). These rolling plains were formed, over time, by sediment (rock particles) moving down from the Andes. In places, the sediment soil is over 1,000 feet (300 m) deep.

Geology of South America

Scientists believe that, around 250 million years ago, Earth's continents were joined together in one giant landmass called Pangaea. Later, Pangaea broke up as the plates of Earth's crust bearing the continents drifted apart. Around 110 million years ago, South America and Africa split apart and the Atlantic Ocean was slowly formed.

Around 170 million years ago, the plate bearing South America collided with the plate bearing the Pacific Ocean. The Pacific plate was forced under the South American plate, forming a deep undersea trench, the Atacama Trench. Deep inside Earth, this plunging ocean crust melted to form molten rock that then welled up inland, forming a line of volcanoes, the Andes Mountains. The highest peaks of the Andes rise 40,000 feet (12,200 m) above the floor of the Atacama Trench, 200 miles (320 km) away.

CHECK THESE OUT!
✔CONTINENT ✔EARTHQUAKE
✔NORTH AMERICA ✔PANGAEA ✔PLATE TECTONICS
✔RIVER ✔TROPICAL REGION ✔VOLCANO

Space

The part of the space–time continuum experienced in only three dimensions

Space has different meanings in different branches of science. For mathematicians and physicists, space describes the range of locations at which an object can be found. Astronomers use "space" to mean the Universe—the planets, stars, galaxies, and the gaps between them.

In everyday experience, the location of any point in space can be found using just three coordinates. From a fixed point or "origin," another point can be reached by moving a certain distance in three directions, each at right angles (90 degrees) to the other two. A box, for example, has length, height, and depth. From one corner, the opposite corner can be defined by these measurements. While space appears to have only three dimensions—length, height, and depth—it is fundamentally connected to time, in four-dimensional space–time.

Classical physics and the Universe

Until the 17th century, most people accepted the model of the Universe first proposed by the Greek philosopher Aristotle (384–322 B.C.E.). Aristotle believed Earth was at the center of the Universe and that the Sun, Moon, and planets orbited Earth in ball-shaped shells. He thought that the outermost shell carried the fixed stars and marked the edge of the Universe.

Ideas began to change with the invention of the telescope. The work of Italian astronomer Galileo Galilei (1564–1642) and others repositioned Earth in orbit around the Sun. Later, astronomers found that some stars showed parallax; in other words, their position in the sky shifted slightly depending on where Earth was in its orbit. This showed that these stars were closer to Earth than most of the others, so the stars must be scattered through space. Suddenly there was no limit to the size of the Universe.

English physicist Sir Isaac Newton (1642–1727) put all this information together to create the theory of universal gravitation, which explained how objects in the Universe attract each other over long distances in proportion to their masses. Newton's laws were based on a

HIGHLIGHTS

◆ Any point in space can be specified from another point using just three coordinates, equivalent to length, height, and depth.

◆ In modern physics, the three dimensions of space are combined with time to create a four-dimensional space–time continuum.

◆ Most space is empty. Physicists once thought it was filled with a substance called ether.

three-dimensional idea of space and began to be challenged by new, more complicated theories in the early 20th century.

Relativity and space–time

The nature of light caused problems in the Universe described by Newton. Most experiments showed that light had the properties of a wave. At the time, people thought that a wave needed a medium to travel through, so if light from distant stars was reaching Earth, space could not be empty. From Newton's time

A sense of three-dimensional space can be re-created using computers. This is called virtual reality.

onward, physicists looked for evidence of the ether (EE-thur)—a substance that they thought filled space and carried light waves.

In the 1880s, American physicists Albert Michelson (1852–1931) and Edward Morley (1838–1923) devised an experiment to prove the existence of the ether by measuring the speed of light with absolute precision. To their surprise, the experiment produced no evidence for the ether, and so demolished the theory. Instead, they discovered something very strange—the speed of light was exactly the same from all directions. This went completely against common sense—Earth is moving through space, so surely light approaching Earth head-on should arrive traveling at a higher relative speed than light "catching up" from behind.

In 1905, German-born U.S. physicist Albert Einstein (1879–1955) made a proposal that turned physics upside down. He proposed that the speed of light was a constant (186,282 miles per second or 299,792 km/s) because it was the absolute speed limit of the Universe. In his theory of relativity, he explored the effects of this and proved that the shape of an object and its mass change depending on the speed at which it travels through space. However, it is only when objects approach the speed of light that these effects become clear.

Einstein's theory revolutionized thinking about space and the Universe, but it was incomplete. Gravity was the problem. According to Newton, this force acted instantly over the largest distances, but this

Looking out from Earth into space, the stars in the Milky Way, Earth's home galaxy, can be seen.

would break the speed limit set by light. To reconcile the two theories, Einstein came up with a new model of space and time—the space–time continuum—in which large masses bend the space–time around them. A star can be imagined as a bowling ball in the middle of a rubber sheet, creating a large dent. The planets in their orbits roll around the contours of this dent in space–time, and even light is bent by it.

In Einstein's day, physicists thought the Universe was a fixed size and had existed forever. All this changed with the discovery that the entire Universe is expanding from an initial "big bang" that created it around 12 billion years ago. According to modern theories, the Universe is a bubble of space expanding and curving around on itself by the mass of material inside it.

CHECK THESE OUT!
✔ASTRONOMY ✔BLACK HOLE ✔ENERGY ✔FORCE ✔GALAXY ✔GRAVITY ✔NEWTONIAN PHYSICS ✔PHYSICS ✔RELATIVITY ✔SPACE SCIENCE ✔UNIVERSE

Space Science

The study of the behavior of matter and living organisms in microgravity conditions

Carrying out experiments in orbit around Earth provides scientists with valuable insights. As well as learning about near-Earth space, orbiting laboratories study physical, chemical, and biological processes to observe how the conditions of space affect them.

Experiments in orbit

The first space science experiments were carried out on board rockets in the 1940s. At the time, rockets were not powerful enough to reach a stable orbit around Earth—the best they could manage was a short hop into space above Earth's atmosphere. This changed in 1957 with the launch of the first orbiting satellite. As astronauts followed in the early 1960s, they were able to carry out complex experiments, and space science became an important part of the space program.

Conditions in Earth's orbit differ in two main ways from those on Earth. The absence of air creates an almost perfect vacuum (VA-KYOOM). The absence of the effects of gravity in space is called microgravity. The contents of an orbiting spacecraft are all falling around Earth at the same speed and so act as if gravity has disappeared.

As the insides of the first spacecraft were cramped, space science was limited to simple experiments carried out on automatic satellites. Satellites could also measure the conditions in space around them and provide information about Earth by photographing the weather and by remote sensing Earth's surface. Then, in the early 1970s, the Soviet Union launched the first permanent space station, called *Salyut 1*. The first U.S. station, *Skylab*, was launched in 1973, and astronauts carried out experiments there for a year. Today, over a dozen countries are working on the International Space Station project. This will act as an orbiting laboratory for space-based science. The completed station will include power generators and three research laboratories. Its crew will spend 120 hours per week working on research operations.

Space biology

Experiments to investigate the effect of microgravity on living organisms, including astronauts, give scientists a better understanding of how life functions. This also helps them to counteract the health hazards of space travel.

All organisms have evolved to function in Earth's gravitational field. Animal circulation relies on gravity to take blood to the lowest parts of the body, and plants rely on gravity to pull their roots down into the soil. When removed from the pull of gravity, circulation decreases and plant roots grow in random directions. Some insects, for unknown reasons, hatch fewer eggs and do not live as long in space. Many body tissues do not work as efficiently in space. For example, muscles waste because they are not working against gravity, and white blood cells lose their ability to fight some invading diseases. Some bacteria thrive in microgravity, so there is increased danger of infection in space. Medicines, diet supplements, and vigorous exercise can counter some of these problems.

HIGHLIGHTS

◆ Space has two advantages for science—access to a near-perfect vacuum and microgravity conditions.

◆ Space-based biology studies how organisms function and develop in the absence of gravity.

◆ Space doctors are working to understand and combat the health hazards that the absence of gravity creates for astronauts.

◆ Substances can be manufactured with greater purity and perfection in space than on Earth.

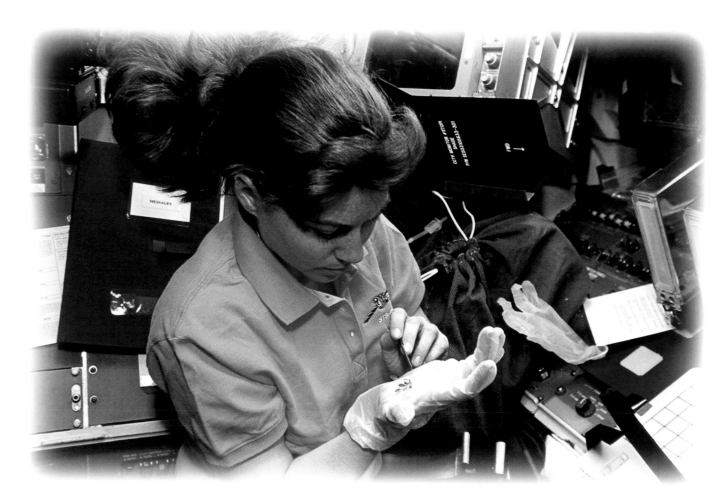

An astronaut on board the Space Shuttle Columbia *studies how a plant shoot grows in microgravity.*

Space sickness, which feels similar to motion sickness, is a problem for many astronauts. Scientists think that the sickness is caused by conflicting signals coming from the eyes, nervous system, and inner ear (where the body's balance sensors are located). The problem fades in a few days, as the brain adjusts to the new conditions.

Space physics

The absence of gravity makes physical materials behave in different ways. It removes two important effects—sedimentation and convection. Sedimentation pulls dense particles to the bottom of a mixture, while convection causes less dense materials to rise above denser ones. The absence of these effects has a range of possibilities for manufacturing. For example, alloys (mixtures of different metals) are never perfect on Earth because gravity separates the heavier and lighter atoms before the metal can solidify. In addition, there is less chance of contamination (introduction of unwanted substances) in space-based manufacturing because materials float and do not need to be held in containers. Several space missions have manufactured perfect alloy samples.

One final important application of microgravity is in crystal manufacture. Crystals are manufactured by dissolving a suitable substance in a liquid, and then injecting solid "seeds" of the substance. Atoms and molecules fall out of the solution and add themselves to this seed. When a crystal is grown in a laboratory on Earth, it develops flaws as gravity and convection currents in the solution cause movement. In space, flawless crystals can be grown, ranging from organic proteins to semiconductors.

CHECK THESE OUT!
✔DENSITY ✔NASA ✔REMOTE SENSING ✔SATELLITE ✔SEMICONDUCTOR ✔SPACE STATION

Space Station

A vehicle orbiting Earth that is visited by astronauts using other spacecraft

Space stations have been one of the most useful developments of the space program in the former Soviet Union and the United States. Unlike a short-duration spacecraft mission, space stations offer semi-permanent platforms in space where astronauts can work for months at a time, carrying out a range of experiments and investigating the effects of long exposure to the conditions of space.

Early space stations

The idea of orbital cities where hundreds of people could live and work was proposed by scientists and writers long before the space age of 1957 onwards. Stations like this might have become a reality, but other areas of technology overtook them, with computers and machines providing cheaper and more efficient alternatives to tasks previously done by people.

The first space station was the Soviet *Salyut 1*, launched on April 19, 1971, aboard a Proton rocket. The project did not go well. The first mission to *Salyut* was aborted (called off), and three cosmonauts (Russian astronauts) on the second mission were killed in an accident as they returned to Earth. *Salyut 1* was allowed to reenter orbit and burn up in October 1971. *Salyut 2* and *3* were the first military space stations and also ran into problems. *Salyut 2* broke up before it could enter its proper orbit and *Salyut 3*'s docking equipment soon failed.

Skylab

While the Russians were having difficulties, NASA was working to catch up. NASA had been planning its space station, called *Skylab*, since the late 1960s but delayed its launch until the end of the Apollo Moon program. *Skylab* was launched

An artist's impression of how the International Space Station will look when all its modules have been put into orbit and assembled.

HIGHLIGHTS

◆ The first space station was *Salyut 1*, launched by the Soviet Union in April 1971.

◆ The United States launched *Skylab*, a station built out of recycled rocket parts, in 1973.

◆ In 1986, the Soviet Union launched *Mir*, the first modular space station, with four laboratory modules around a central command area.

◆ The International Space Station is owned by several space agencies from around the world.

on May 14, 1973, but it ran into immediate problems. The station's sunshield accidentally activated during launch, and the rush of air tore it away, taking a solar panel with it. The station reached orbit safely, but temperatures inside varied wildly without its insulating equipment. In addition, the other main solar panel failed to open. The first crew (*Skylab 2*) were able to put a replacement sunshield in place and fix the remaining solar panel during a daring spacewalk. The *Skylab 2* crew stayed aboard the station for 28 days, setting a new space endurance record.

During the next two missions, the astronauts carried out experiments in space biology and physics, observed Earth, and monitored their own responses to prolonged weightlessness. *Skylab* was finally abandoned in February 1974 and crashed back to Earth in July 1979.

Later Soviet stations

From *Salyut 4* onward, the Soviet program began to have better results. *Salyut 4* was an astronomy station, fitted with a wide range of instruments.

Two crews visited it on Soyuz rockets, and the crew of *Soyuz 18B* set a new endurance record of 62 days in 1975. *Salyut 5* was the last military space station, while *Salyut 6*, launched in 1977, was the first station to be fitted with two docking ports. These allowed the crew's spacecraft to remain docked at one point while automatic cargo ferries brought supplies and new equipment. As a result, the length of space station missions increased rapidly—the crew of *Soyuz 32* stayed aboard for 175 days. *Salyut 7* brought further improvements and new records.

Before *Salyut 7* was launched, the Soviet Union was already planning a new and more ambitious station. *Mir*, meaning peace, was launched in 1986 and was the first modular (containing separate parts) space station. The main body of the station was fitted with six docking ports, which allowed four extra modules to be attached to the station once it was in orbit. These modules carried laboratories for experiments in space science and manufacturing.

The International Space Station

NASA had always planned to build a new space station using the Space Shuttle *Atlantis*, but problems and budget cuts meant that the station, *Freedom*, was delayed through the 1980s and 1990s. With the break-up of the Soviet Union and a new spirit of cooperation with Russia, the idea began to form of combining Russian space station experience and launch vehicles with U.S. money to create an International Space Station (ISS). From 1995 onward, *Atlantis* made several missions to visit *Mir*. The *Mir* station fell into disrepair in the late 1990s and was abandoned for a time. In February 2001 it was brought down into the Pacific Ocean.

Various other countries are now involved with the ISS, including the European and Japanese space agencies, Canada, and Brazil. The International Space Station is the most ambitious space project since the Moon landings, involving nearly 50 launches over several years. Although the station has been permanently crewed since 2000, it will not be complete until 2006.

CHECK THESE OUT!
✔APOLLO MISSION ✔NASA ✔SPACE SCIENCE

Spectroscopy

The study of the electromagnetic radiation given off by atoms and molecules

When a piece of potassium is placed in the flame of a gas burner, it vaporizes and adds a purple color to the flame. In the same situation, a piece of sodium produces a yellow flame. Different elements and compounds give off light of different colors when energy (such as heat from the gas flame) is supplied to them. A solution of copper sulfate appears blue because it absorbs the red and green portions of white light. These ideas are the basis of spectroscopy (spek-TRAH-skuh-pee), which is a method of identifying chemicals by the light (or other radiation) they emit (give off) or absorb.

The science of spectroscopy

Atoms consist of a central nucleus surrounded by a cloud of electrons that sit in energy levels rather like the rungs of a ladder. Normally, an atom has the lowest possible amount of energy and is said to be in its ground state. This means the electrons sit on the lowest rungs of the energy ladder. If energy is supplied to the atom

Spectrometers are used in medicine. They can identify chemicals present in samples of body fluid.

(for example, by heating it or shining light of the right wavelength on it), some of the outer electrons move farther away from the nucleus, climbing to higher rungs of the energy ladder. The atom is said to be in an excited state.

An excited atom is unstable and rapidly returns to its ground state. The electrons that moved away from the nucleus move back toward it, giving off the energy that they took in before. The electrons in an atom cannot have just any amount of energy. They cannot sit anywhere, only on the rungs of the energy ladder, so an atom gives off (or takes in) only certain fixed amounts of energy, which are equal to the difference in energy between two rungs of the energy ladder. These fixed amounts of energy are called quanta (one is called a quantum), and they are different for each atom. Each quantum of energy produces light (or other electromagnetic radiation) of a particular color.

It is now possible to understand why potassium metal burns with a purple flame. When potassium atoms are heated, their electrons move to higher rungs on the energy ladder. These excited atoms rapidly return to

---

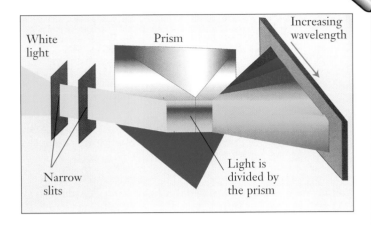

White light separates into a spectrum of colors when it is passed through a prism.

their ground state, giving off quanta of electromagnetic radiation. For potassium, this radiation is purple light.

Types of spectroscopes

Holding materials in a flame is one of the oldest types of spectroscopy. More modern methods use sophisticated equipment and can identify chemicals even in tiny quantities. The equipment used for spectroscopy is called a spectroscope and has several distinct parts. Light or other radiation produced by the sample chemical is passed through a prism (a triangular block of glass) or a diffraction grating (a series of thin slits in plastic or glass). These split the light into its different wavelengths. The result, focused on a screen, is a series of lines, each of which may have a different color. The pattern of lines is called an emission spectrum and gives information about how the chemical's atoms behave when they emit energy.

Some types of spectroscopes put their results onto a piece of photographic film instead of a screen. These are called spectrographs. Other similar devices called spectrometers use electronic detectors instead of film.

Pioneers of spectroscopy

Many scientists helped to establish the modern science of spectroscopy. English physicist Sir Isaac Newton (1642–1727) discovered that a prism splits white light into a spectrum of colors. When German scientist Joseph von Fraunhofer (1787–1826) passed sunlight through a thin vertical slit, he saw a pattern of dark lines and

LOOK CLOSER

Studying the Stars

When Joseph von Fraunhofer (pictured below) made his studies of the Sun's spectrum, he invented a new way of studying the stars. Spectroscopy is now widely used by astronomers to study the light given off by stars and planets. This reveals the chemicals present in their atmosphere or on their surface. As well as containing a gigantic optical telescope, NASA's Hubble Space Telescope contains spectroscopic equipment for making detailed observations of the stars and planets at which it is directed.

realized that each one was made by a different wavelength (color) of light being absorbed by atoms in the Sun's atmosphere.

The method of studying the colors of a chemical's flame was pioneered by two German physicists in the 1850s. Gustav Kirchoff (1824–1887) and Robert Bunsen (1811–1899) found that different substances burned with colored lights when placed in the flame of a Bunsen burner (a gas burner newly invented by Bunsen). Later, they found they could pass this light through a diffraction grating to make a unique pattern of lines for each chemical. In this way, they discovered two new metals, cesium (SEE-zee-uhm; Cs) and rubidium (Rb).

It was not until the 19th century that the mathematical theory of spectroscopy was worked out. After studying the spectrum produced by hydrogen, Swiss school teacher Johann Balmer (1825–1898) worked out a simple formula for calculating the wavelengths of light given off. Later, it was found that a similar formula could be used for other chemical elements as well.

CHECK THESE OUT!
✔ATOM ✔ELECTROMAGNETIC SPECTRUM ✔ELECTRON
✔ENERGY ✔NEWTONIAN PHYSICS ✔OPTICS

Star

A large ball of gas in space that shines because of internal nuclear reactions

Balls of gas that usually shine by releasing energy through nuclear reactions in their core are called stars. Unlike most other objects in the sky, stars produce light instead of simply reflecting it. Although the sky may appear to be full of stars, in reality only a few thousand stars can be seen from Earth with the naked eye.

Studying stars

Since ancient times, astrologers and astronomers have divided stars into groups, or constellations, representing mythical figures, animals, and other objects. They range from faint stars close to Earth to brilliant ones many miles away. The stars in a single constellation are not related to each other. They would look very different if viewed from elsewhere in the galaxy.

Astronomers once thought that the stars were relatively close to Earth, lying a little way beyond the planets. However, the arrival of the telescope meant a revolution in understanding stars.

Once astronomers realized that Earth was moving around the Sun rather than the other way around, they had a simple way of measuring the distance to stars. Opposite sides of Earth's

orbit are 186 million miles (300 million km) apart, so a star observed at six-month intervals should have different positions in the sky because of the changing point of view from Earth—an effect called parallax (PAR-uh-LAKS). When astronomers looked for parallax, they found that there was none for most stars, indicating that they were incredibly far away. However, a few stars did show measurable parallax. This proved that the stars were scattered through space at various distances from Earth.

Accurate distances allowed astronomers to work out the magnitude (brightness) of stars and proved they were often as bright as or brighter than the Sun.

Color, makeup, and mass

Stars have a wide range of colors, from red to blue. Red stars are either very faint or very bright, blue stars are nearly always very bright, and yellow stars such as the Sun have average brightness.

Passing starlight through a prism (PRI-zuhm; transparent body that splits light beams) to create a rainbowlike spectrum revealed more information. Dark lines across the spectrum correspond to elements in the star's atmosphere, which absorb light of certain wavelengths and colors. Astronomers realized that the elements detected in a star were closely connected to its color and magnitude. Some stars also had their spectra shifted slightly to the red end of the spectrum. This redshift was caused by the stars moving rapidly away from Earth.

Binary stars—pairs of stars in orbit around each other—can be used by astronomers to gain information about star masses and sizes. Fortunately, most stars in Earth's galaxy are in

HIGHLIGHTS

- There are billions of stars in Earth's galaxy alone, but just a few thousand can be seen from Earth with the naked eye.

- Stars such as the Sun are large balls of hydrogen and helium gas. They vary considerably in brightness, mass, size, and color.

- Astronomers can work out what stage a star has reached in its life cycle by measuring its brightness and color.

- When stars such as the Sun get old, they form red giants and then white dwarfs. Bigger stars explode in supernovas.

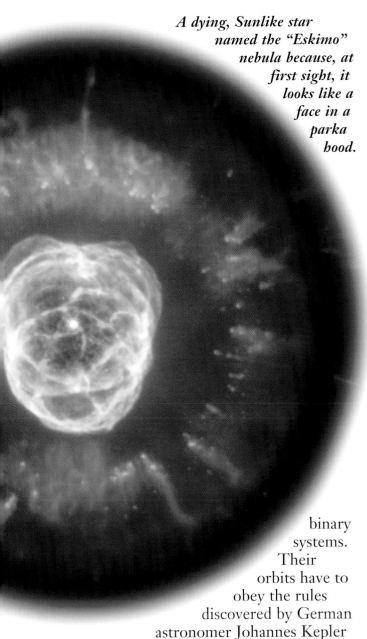

A dying, Sunlike star named the "Eskimo" nebula because, at first sight, it looks like a face in a parka hood.

fainter than the Sun to 100,000 times brighter, and their diameters from just a few miles across (for superdense neutron stars), through the size of Earth (for white dwarfs) to over one thousand times the size of the Sun (supergiants). Masses, however, have a much more limited range— from 1/10 to 50 Sun masses. The colors of stars relate directly to their surface temperatures. Blue stars have the hottest surfaces, up to 54,000°F (30,000°C), and red ones the coolest, as low as 5500°F (3000°C).

Life cycles

Stars are born in huge interstellar clouds of gas and dust called nebulae (NE-byuh-LEE). The formation of a star may be triggered by a shock wave, perhaps from a distant exploding star, passing through the cloud. Slowly, a cloud of hydrogen and helium gas begins to collapse under its own gravity, pulling in more material around it. As more gas falls into the middle of the cloud, the pressure and temperature begin to rise, and the star begins to give out heat. Eventually, the heat and pressure in the star's central core get high enough to trigger nuclear fusion in which hydrogen atoms are forced together to form helium atoms, releasing energy.

As the star begins to shine properly, it joins what scientists call the main sequence, which is

binary systems. Their orbits have to obey the rules discovered by German astronomer Johannes Kepler (1571–1630) and English physicist Sir Isaac Newton (1642–1727). The orbital period of a binary system and the distances of the two stars from the center of mass (the balance point of the system) can therefore be used to work out the masses of both stars in the system.

Putting it all together

The results of all these different measurements show that stars have a huge range of properties. Their brightnesses range from 100,000 times

Star charts can be used to identify constellations and individual stars such as the North Star (Polaris).

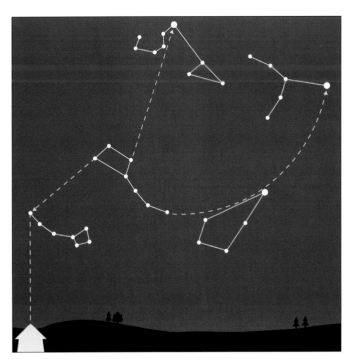

Star Atlases and Catalogs

Although some stars still have names, all are now classified according to entries in star atlases and catalogs. A star atlas shows the positions and magnitude (brightness) of stars in the sky, usually using different sized circles to represent different brightnesses of stars. Constellations are still used; however, by international agreement, they are no longer patterns of specific stars, but simply areas of the sky. Every star in the sky belongs to one constellation or another. Stars are cataloged in a variety of ways. The simplest method gives bright stars a Greek letter according to their brightness within a constellation. The brightest star is alpha, the next beta, and so on. The Greek alphabet has only 24 letters, so beyond that, stars in a constellation are numbered.

the phase in which stars spend most of their lives. Bigger stars will burn their hydrogen fuel more fiercely, releasing blue light, while smaller ones will burn steadily, producing yellow light. Astronomers know that blue stars must use up their fuel quickly, and swiftly move on to the next stage in their life cycle because there are fewer bright blue stars than fainter yellow ones. However, a star such as the Sun will shine steadily for 10 billion years before it too uses up all the hydrogen fuel in its core. When a star of

An image from the Hubble Space Telescope of a cluster of stars in a small galaxy close to Earth's.

whatever mass reaches this stage, it will swell to around a hundred times its original size, becoming a giant. The star's brightness increases but its surface temperature drops, so most giant stars are red. Eventually, the temperature in the star's core will increase until it can start to burn helium. This helium-burning stage, where the star shrinks back to normal, is very short compared to a star's overall lifespan. At its end, the star will swell back to form a red giant again.

Dead stars

Stars die in very different ways depending on their masses. Stars such as the Sun swell as they use up their helium, puffing off their outer layers and leaving behind a planet-sized core called a white dwarf, which slowly cools down over millions of years. More massive stars can continue to make energy by fusing together heavier elements until they eventually begin to fuse iron atoms. Iron is the first element whose fusion absorbs rather than releases energy. As the giant star's power source is cut off, it collapses on itself before exploding in a huge supernova. All that is left behind is a tiny, superdense neutron star that is several times heavier than the Sun and concentrated in a sphere the size of a city. Sometimes a black hole is formed, a tiny and incredibly dense point in space where gravity is so strong that not even light can escape it.

CHECK THESE OUT!
✔ASTRONOMY ✔CONSTELLATION ✔COSMIC RAY
✔COSMOLOGY ✔FUSION ✔GALAXY ✔GRAVITY
✔RED GIANT ✔SOLAR SYSTEM ✔SPECTROSCOPY
✔TELESCOPE ✔UNIVERSE ✔WHITE DWARF

Glossary

ammonia (uh-MOH-nee-uh) Pungent, colorless gas; a compound of nitrogen and hydrogen.

communications satellite Humanmade satellite used to send telephone calls and radio and television programs between distant parts of the world.

detonator (DEH-tuh-NAY-tuhr) Device used to set off (detonate) an explosive.

diode (DY-ohd) Electronic device with two terminals; used to make current flow in one direction.

displacement (dih-SPLAY-smuhnt) Measurement of the movement of an object or substance.

double-planet system Two planets that are held in one another's orbits.

electromagnet Magnet created by passing an electric current through a wire surrounding a core of magnetic material.

gamma rays Photons emitted by a radioactive substance. Part of the electromagnetic spectrum.

gene (JEEN) Strand of DNA code for one inherited characteristic.

graptolite (GRAP-tuh-lyt) Small, extinct, water-dwelling animals.

headwaters The part of a river near its source.

invertebrate (IN-VUHR-tuh-bruht) Animal with no backbone.

lagoon (luh-GOON) Shallow pond or channel that is near or part of a larger body of water.

lattice (LA-tuhs) Regular arrangement, such as that of the atoms in a crystal.

leeward Facing in the direction that the prevailing wind blows.

light-year Distance light travels in a year through a vacuum (5.88 trillion miles or 9.46 trillion kilometers).

loch Gaelic word meaning lake.

magnitude Size or quality; also the brightness of a star.

mollusk Any of a large group of invertebrate animals (such as snails, clams, or squids) with a soft unsegmented body usually enclosed in a hard shell.

nervous system System in vertebrates made up of the brain, spinal cord, and nerves; how the body receives and responds to outside stimuli.

neutral Neither acid nor alkaline. Also, having no electrical charge.

nuclear reactor Device for the release of nuclear energy.

parallax Difference in apparent direction of an object as seen from two points far apart.

photon (FOH-tuhn) Packet of light energy.

radiation Process of emitting radiant energy in the form of waves or particles.

refraction (rih-FRAK-shuhn) Apparent bending of light as it passes from one medium to another.

relative motion Apparent direction and speed of a moving object when observed from different points.

residue (REH-zuh-DOO) Material left behind.

shale Type of rock formed by the consolidation of clay, mud, or silt.

soil erosion Wearing away of the top layer of soil by water, wind, or glacial ice.

solar panel Sheet made up of cells that convert sunlight into electrical energy.

space walk Excursion outside the spacecraft by an astronaut in space.

transistor Device that controls the flow of electricity in electronic equipment.

white hot Incandescing (glowing) white when heated to a certain temperature.

windward Facing in the direction the prevailing wind blows from.

Index

Page numbers in **boldface type** refer to main articles and their illustrations. Page numbers in *italic type* refer to additional illustrations.

550
EXP
#9

Exploring Earth & Space

05/06	DATE DUE		